Before You Cast
the Second Stone

by

Klaus Heck

Library of Congress No. 79-84181

ISBN Number - 0-915948-05-2

© Klaus Heck 1979

WESTERN NORTH CAROLINA PRESS
DILLSBORO, NORTH CAROLINA
28725

Table of Contents

PROLOGUE

A Post Card From New York

Alexander Holuka. There was no doubt about it. For the fifth time the old man picked up the post card, turned it over and examined it carefully. But it told him no more than it actually said: "Merry Christmas, Alex Holuka." It was postmarked: "12-12-62 New York, N. Y." Part of the stamp was torn off. The brief message was written in clumsy Cyrillic letters and, had it not been for the clearly legible postmark, it might indeed have been a practical joke. The photograph on the other side showed New York in color. With his somewhat dim eyes Igor looked at the fantastic skyscrapers that stood out against a brilliant blue sky. He scratched his head and tried to smooth down his unruly blond hair. Then he took the card and stepped out of the house. As he gazed along the railway tracks into the distance, he was acutely aware of his loneliness. It was hard not to have anyone with whom he could share the card. He shuffled over to his little vegetable patch, sat down on the wooden bench and dug into his pockets for a few sunflower seeds. As he sat there, chewing and spitting, his thoughts turned back.

1942. He counted on his fingers and found it hard to believe that twenty years had passed since Alex, at the age of fifteen, had left him. From Llwov in the Ukraine, the boy's parents had sent him here to his uncle to escape the advancing battlefront and a possible premature and senseless induction into the Red army. Alex had never seen his uncle before; he had only heard him described as a queer duck who, in the twenties, at the time of the Ukrainian famine, had left his family and gone off somewhere to the east, to earn his meager living as a flagman. Igor had married, but his wife had died three years later just at the time he had taken on this job in Isbitze. So here he was master of Isbitze, his own master, for Isbitze had no other inhabitants. It was a single-track loading station about an hour south of Voronesh, not far from the river Don. The flagman's cottage lay in the midst of an endless steppe; only in the distance could a border of woodland be seen. Since it was a flag station, there was not much real work to be done except in fall and winter when wood was loaded. The nearest settlement was Malinovska, a half-hour's trip by bicycle, but even Malinovska had only fifty inhabitants. In the course of the years, Igor had grown used to his solitude, until one day Alex arrived.

Alex gave a new meaning to his life. He loved him like a son. He wanted to tell him all he knew about life, and he did everything for him that was in his power. But it was only a few months before the war, and the German front pushed all the way out here to the Don. During the winter of '42 to '43, while outside in the bitter cold German soldiers were loading wood, Igor and the boy sat beside the radio and heard about the heroic battle of Stalingrad. Heroic for both sides, Igor had tried to impress upon the boy.

Alex knew something about the Germans. His mother, who was Austrian, had told him enough about them so that he could not hate them. He knew that with Germany it might be possible to form a united front against Bolshevism. Hatred of Communist Russians had long since been implanted in him. All too often, however, Uncle Igor was unable to give proper answers to his endless questions. And, thinking back now, Igor found everything still more complicated. Today Nikita Khrushchev was head of the Soviet Union; less than a generation ago he was Murderer No. 1 of the Ukraine. The Germans were now back in their country and half of them, so it seemed, were Communists, while the other half were capitalists. The Ukraine was entirely Russian, and a large slice of Poland had been pushed over to the West. Igor kept scratching his head. He no longer understood the world.

Again he became aware of the card in his hand, and suddenly he remembered the day Alex left. They had celebrated Christmas together and then trudged through the deep snow to Malinovska. There they had inspected the German bunkers which today stood empty and deserted, as though waiting for a new mission. With the Russian peasants they had sat around the radio. He, Igor, owned a radio that he had brought from Isbitze. Apprehensively they had followed the course of the war.

On that evening a message had come from Llwov. A German soldier had brought the letter. Alex's parents told Igor that they were going to try to escape to Austria. They urged him to explain to Alex that their future lay in the West, no longer in the Ukraine. They begged Alex to escape with the help of the Germans, to make his way to Austria and meet them there at the home of relatives. Alex was obliged to reach a decision, like a man.

A few days later he was a stowaway on one of the last German trains that Igor dispatched from Isbitze. Igor waved to him for the last time. Hope, joy, the content and meaning of life departed with Alex, and the loneliness of Igor's self-chosen retreat covered him like a shroud.

That was 20 years ago—and now this post card. "They're alive; they're all alive!" he chuckled, with tears in his eyes. And suddenly he felt impelled to do something kind. His glance fell upon a small birchwood cross at the corner of the toolshed. He took a rake and cleared away the winter's protective covering of brush from the grave, exposing the first spring shoots to the sun. The grave bore no name. Only he and Alex knew that it was the grave of a German.

Chapter One
MY YOUTH

I am writing this book for my wife, my children, my friends and all those who are fascinated by a true story of Europe's recent history. But I am also writing it for another reason. Since I have been living in America, I have found considerable interest among all circles, young or old, in a first-hand account of what it was like to grow up in Nazi Germany and live through the war. Ignorance and preconceived notions about the Germans of the Hitler era still persist and often make it difficult for me not to conceal my origin. Even today, residual propaganda influences and a deep distrust often blocks the way to a better understanding between two peoples. And so I am writing for all those who have a right to ask me: "What did you do then?" We Germans bear a terrible burden, and sometimes I find a certain comfort in the fact that more than 200,000 Germans also lost their lives in Hitler's concentration camps because of their opposition to him. This is almost twice the number who acted as Hitler's henchmen during those war years.

I was not a radical, not a fanatic. I was what one might call a typical German, just as I presume my American friends regard themselves as typical Americans. I am an inveterate storyteller; and so I shall try to describe the world as I saw it then. I shall explain what seems necessary to give my American readers a better understanding of the situation, but I beg their indulgence if I describe events from my perspective at the time, events which twenty-five years later proved false.

If I had known then what I know now, I should have tried to dissuade my mother from paying 1,000,000 marks for my baby carriage, since the inflation was nearing its end in 1923 when I was born in Düsseldorf on the Rhein. My brother Hans was three years older than I. We were a family that, on the basis of my father's job and my parents' interests and attitudes toward life, could be labeled as middle class. The German

Children's Caffee Klatch.
Klaus second from right
first row middle is
Peter Sussman (Jewish).

inflation of those years was comparable to that of the American depression. Mother later told us how hopeless everything seemed. Money had no value; foreign troops were occupying Germany; unemployment and misery were the aftermath of the lost war. My father had been at the front for four years. After the war, in 1918, he had the good fortune to obtain a position in one of the largest German iron works. This offered him many different possibilities, for he was an energetic, purposeful and successful man. As a rule, he kept away from politics and social obligations. Once, he and my mother attended a political affair at which a certain man named Hitler shouted his convictions at the crowd in a courageous and rabble-rousing manner. My father found him vulgar and uncultivated. Mother had the impression that he was a fanatic and an idealist, yet she felt that such persons were better than the mealymouthed ones who never came up with a solution to Germany's problems. The fracturing of political Germany into innumerable parties had caused the various parliaments and the Reichstag to degenerate into assemblies of undisciplined shouters. People longed for the order of the pre-war years. They hoped for a new Bismarck, a strong personality.

My childhood was carefree. True, mother had difficulty serving us wholesome meals, and my ankles, which were always bloody where I scraped them with my heels, were a sign that I was suffering from the "English disease." This expression for scrofula probably arose during the time of the British blockade against Germany. In 1929 my father built a magnificent house in Cologne. He could afford it because his firm, which had business connections in Holland, paid his salary in good Dutch guilders. But then the American depression hit Europe. Father's face became lined and careworn. He changed his job and we moved to Stuttgart. However, at this time we were still living with governess, cook and chauffeur, the latter laboring over our heavy Buick. In his leisure hours, Father was a devotee and collector of art.

In 1931 my father died suddenly of a heart attack at the age of fortysix. Since he had just switched to another firm, my mother was not entitled to a pension. It was a severe blow. Even my brother, aged eleven, and I, aged eight, realized that our world would now change radically. Mother bought a big apartment house with the money we had. The income from that and the rent from our house in Cologne made it possible for us to live without dipping into our capital. Mother adjusted courageously to our new situation.

Like most of my friends, I joined the CVIM, a Christian youth movement that represented a sort of cross between YMCA and Boy Scouts. In 1933, when I was ten years old, I transferred from public school to the Gymnasium, which corresponds approximately to the fifth grade. In the Gymnasium one studies a foreign language, usually Latin and, the following year, French. Girls went to the Lyceum. At this age, we boys were little impressed by girls. School was strict, but interesting.

Sports and German history were rather prominent in the curriculum. My favorite subjects were art and music. Hitler had come into power by now. In school we were given the details. Everybody seemed enthusiastic because, at last, something was being done. In fact, a great deal was being done. First of all, the various youth organizations were dissolved and absorbed into the Hitler Jugend. Our CVIM leader explained the reason for this: We're all in the same boat. We must forget our

Klaus age 10; Hans age 13 in April 1933, Dusseldorf.

differences, no matter what they are. Once again we can be proud to be Germans. If we all pull together, we shall be strong. Hitler's hopes lie in the young people. There is room for everyone in the Hitler Jugend. We have offered to serve as leaders in the H.J. because you have confidence in us and because we do not wish to lose our Christian influence over you. The Church is in favor of this. First and foremost we are Germans and then Protestants or Catholics."

Point 16 of the Party program of the NSDAP* stated that the Party was in favor of positive Christianity, but it did not commit itself to any particular creed.

From the age of ten to fourteen we belonged to the junior HJ, from fourteen to eighteen to the Hitler Jugend proper. No one was coerced. I can remember only a few boys and girls who did not belong. We regretted having to give up our green uniforms which were now dyed dark blue. Our

---

*National Socialist German Worker Party

activities were the same. There were camping trips into the nearby countryside; once there was even a trip into Holland. We learned discipline and the fun of shared experiences. We fought with long, thin, bamboo sticks, and those who excelled in this were permitted to wear the sticks like sabers with their uniforms. We had a little flag and a landsknecht's drum.* Our leaders played the guitar and we learned songs of different countries and ages. All in all, it was great fun. There was no word about politics.

In school, a few of the older teachers disappeared and young ones took their places. Insignia were worn by all and often became status symbols. There were, first of all, the old war decorations, then the Party insignia; those with gold edges were the old fighters. The men who had engaged in bloody battles for the Party during its fighting days wore blood badges. There were countless winter-relief insignia, which showed that one had given one's share.

In history class the teacher spoke of the Versailles Treaty and the Boer War in South Africa with its British concentration camps. The German military of all periods was held up as a model. For the semiweekly religious instruction we were separated into two classes: the Catholics were taught by a clergyman, the Protestants by a history teacher. The attitude toward the church was: let the somewhat narrowminded older ones die out; the young generation will no longer succumb to the influence of the church. Priests were smiled at rather condescendingly, and of nuns and monks it was whispered that they were all homosexuals.

H.J. Sunday duties increased. There were marches through the city or drives for the winter-relief fund. Nobody wanted to ask to be excused from these by saying he had to go to church. "Church-going is for old people. A new age has dawned!" We loved the Christmas holidays and their traditions, but the HJ offered new festivals that were said to be older than Christianity: the summer solstice, the harvest festival. Old Germanic words such as Yul, Meet, Ting, Thor, Wotan were bandied about; given names such as Edda, Wulf, Ditmar, Brunhilde, and Elke became fashionable. We carved runes* into the bark of trees. Vikings, Gothic kings and Klaus Störtebecken were held up as paragons. Our parents tried to put all this lofty sentiment into its proper perspective. Our intellectual friends supported Mother in this; and for us, as for many of my friends, the new trend was soon ridiculed and dismissed as so much hullabaloo.

In 1936 we moved back to Cologne, to our lovely house which Mother had been renting. I was now in the H.J. proper, but the more my personal interests began absorbing my attention, the less enthusiastic I was about

---

*Landsknecht refers to a medieval mercenary soldier.
**Old Germanic symbol

my duties in the HJ. My new friend was Peter Rubach. We sat together in school. He was an incredibly gifted violinist and practiced many hours a day. Professor Eldering, his teacher, had a considerable reputation. Through Peter I became acquainted with the world of classical music. This led to opera, and opera led to theatre. We spent many evenings as "extras" on the stage of the Cologne theatre.

In 1937 I spent my summer vacation in England as an exchange student. The English family I lived with was delightful. Once an uncle of theirs came to visit, and when the conversation turned to Hitler, he asked me how we could possibly tolerate such a monster, such a bandit, at the head of our government. I was so surprised and chagrined that I burst into tears, since I found it impossible, with my limited English, to explain how we respected Hitler and how much he had done for us Germans. In truth, everything looked rosy in Germany. There was no unemployment; magnificent highways were being built; cities were being improved; there was new housing for workers and they were able to undertake voyages which were paid for largely by the labor front, a sort of national union. The Austrian Anschluss* was hailed by all, and we were glad for our Austrian brothers, thousands of whom we saw in the illustrated weeklies, welcoming our soldiers as they marched in. "One people, one nation, one Führer." Everyone felt a deep satisfaction at the thought that so much had been accomplished. Every speech of Hitler contained assurances of peace; churches included him in their prayers; we were convinced that a lucky star had sent us this man. My English friend Eric paid me a return visit in 1938. Together we had the opportunity of seeing Hitler in Cologne. Eric was undoubtedly tremendously impressed by the enthusiasm of the tens of thousands who acclaimed Hitler at the railway station.

A number of events now became decisive for me. Confirmation marked the end of my childhood. On Sundays I now wore long pants. In school the teachers changed from the paternal *du* to the more respectful *Sie* when they addressed us. Mother Nature made it clear to me that I had become a young man. I attended dancing class and placed my first kiss upon responsive lips. We learned the foxtrot, the Viennese waltz, the slow waltz, the tango and the two-step. The political scene was now more attentively observed and what I saw was partly magnificent, partly abominable.

Hitler propaganda was cleverly designed to appeal to young people. Though we were no more than members of the Hitler Jugend, ideas were held up to us which were worth striving for: love of home, love of country above all, respect for family, government and officials, purity within and without, veneration of women and mothers, as well as the Hitler motto: "Hard as Krupp steel, tough as leather and swift as

---

Unification of Germany.

greyhounds." Those were not merely slogans or cliches; they were forcefully drilled into us, and living up to them gave us a feeling of superiority.

The huge assemblies and Party celebrations were magnificent and impressive. Martial music, uniforms and titles, discipline and tradition, a strong peasantry, new laws designed to preserve the ancient and honorable traditions of an agrarian society, the Nürnberg law pertaining to the sterilization of the incurably feebleminded and to the checking of foreign racial influences—all this seemed reasonable to us, especially when we were told that the young people of other countries were getting soft, were smoking and drinking and regarding wealth and comfort as their only ideals. When we heard that in France and the U.S.A. young people of different races were inter-marrying, we felt proud of living in a society that did not tolerate idlers, beggars, extremists of any kind and girls who used makeup. The conquest of civilization is necessary, but culture is the bridge that spans the centuries and raises us to a higher level.

We began enthusiastically collecting cigarette coupons in exchange for colored reproductions which, in turn, we pasted into albums. These pictures covered a wide range of subjects: Adolf Hitler's life and the Party; the 1936 Olympic Games in Berlin; German history as represented in famous paintings; Gothic, Renaissance, Baroque and modern paintings. The latter albums were favorites, among my friends at any rate.

We also admired American jazz, though in Party language it was a Negroid expression for primitive eroticism. During this time I improved my English by taking evening courses. One day, a group of American Baptists arrived and we were chosen to take them sightseeing around Cologne. We were not a little surprised to find that more than half of them were Negroes. One evening, when we met them in a hotel lobby, one of the Negroes sat down at the piano and started playing jazz. The entire hotel gathered round and the jazz player made a great hit. It was so unusual to see Negroes in Cologne that when a Swiss guard in the cathedral asked whether these people were Christian and not heathens I did not find the question particularly outlandish. I believe Cologne's only Negro lived in Mother's apartment house. Mr. Goodman was left over from the occupation forces of the First World War. He had married a German but had no children. He made his living in shoe-cream advertising and was self-respecting and generally popular. At this age the Nürnberg Law could not affect him and he was left in peace.

As for the negative aspect of what we saw, it began with the Roehm affair. Although it seemed proper that Hitler should eliminate this SA* big

---

*A division of the NSDAP.

shot because of his homosexual aberrations, we were nonetheless shocked by the extent of the arrests and the nature of the liquidations that followed. It was said that Hitler himself had caught Roehm in flagrante delicto and shot him on the spot. Then came the dismissal of deserving generals, while uncultivated braggarts such as Dr. Ley and Herr Streicher were becoming more and more vocal. Once there was talk of euthanasia, and a few of our acquaintances died suddenly in hospitals where, as incurables, they had led unhappy existences. A number of people, particularly women, addressed letters of protest to Rudolf Hess, Hitler's aide; a bishop protested in an open letter, whereupon the practice of euthanasia was discontinued. Our Nazi block warden became more powerful and more annoying with his everlasting fund-raising. Then we heard of orgies in high Party circles. "If the Führer knew that!" people said.

My brother Hans took part in a professional competition and was thereupon suddenly requested to come to the office of the police commissioner. He was confronted by an HJ leader, a police officer and an SS* officer. They questioned him about his political views, his friends, his foreign connections, and finally warned him never again to write such dangerous nonsense. What had he done? The last question in the competition read: "What do you expect of a good daily paper?" Hans had answered somewhat as follows: "The daily paper, next to the radio, is one of the most important sources of information. Without it, a political opinion cannot be formed. I expect a daily paper first of all to report the facts and then, in editorials, to express different points of view. This helps people form their opinions. Such a newspaper, however, does not exist. In democratic countries newspapers are financed by advertisers. Editorials contradicting the policies of the financing groups would be ruinous for the paper. In Germany, newspapers are supported by the state, in order to keep them free from private influences. Reports must appear in a form approved by the state, since the state is not anxious to breed needless opposition. We as a nation must stick together in grave times. Therefore, what the state recognizes as proper must be accepted if we do not wish to fall back into the chaos of the Weimar era."

With the last sentence Hans felt that he had been particularly diplomatic—but not at all! The sinister-looking representatives of power probably suspected treason in this seventeen year old, for was this not a state in which the Führer was always right? Was not everything that was officially printed beneficial to the broader aim and hence always the truth? The old English motto obtained: Our country, right or wrong.

Hans came home alarmingly pale. Mother advised him to keep his critical impulses to himself in the future. Many people did just that; others came out freely with their opinions and their knowledge, at any rate in

---

*A Nazi political, semi-military elite force.

intimate circles. However, it may be said that whenever unpleasant facts as grievances were reported, the general tendency was to regard them as fifty per cent exaggerated or to pooh-pooh them as mere rumors. This was probably wishful thinking. Mother's enthusiasm for the movement subsided altogether, and I believe she even asked to be dropped from the Party.

I was sixteen years old when I made the acquaintance of Wermer Eckes. He was a little older than I. We first met at the public swimming pool. His father was the head of the local postoffice; his mother could bake the best *stollen* I ever tasted. Werner was thickset and rawboned; sometimes he looked slightly hunchbacked. He was a regular roughneck. He loved sports, football and the Hitler Jugend. He was an enthusiastic champion of everything the government had to say. He wanted to become an HJ leader. He often complained that he was not tall enough for the SS. His parents found all this silly, but they had no real influence over him. They valued his acquaintance with me because, as Mrs. Eckes said, at our house he was exposed to a better environment.

"Baldur von Schierach* visits your neighbors?" Our neighbors, a non-political banker's family, were friends of Schierach. Now and then, he enjoyed calling on them as a private citizen and spending a few hours in an intellectual atmosphere. "Very high class!" Werner observed, and greeted the waiting chauffeur at the impressive Mercedes with "Heil Hitler!"

Oh, Werner, you're so carried away by everything. Lots of my friends feel that things are not as rosy as all that."

"Nonsense, those aren't friends; they're belly-achers. Just think: Berlin, Rome, Tokyo! Nobody can push us around any more."

"Rome?" I said in amazement. "The Duce speaks of friendship and doesn't even give us back our Tyrol. And many people say he's a monomaniac with his eternal shouting about the Imperium."

"Beating the big drum is all part of it, Klaus," Werner laughed. "You're right about the Tyrol. But the Führer wants peace. That'll all straighten itself out eventually."

"Yes, but you must admit the situation in Czechoslovakia and Poland is awful."

"Klaus," Werner answered, "the Poles are a miserable, servile lot. Their messiness is proverbial. And these are the chaps that harrass our countrymen living in that isolated corridor. And as for Czechoslovakia, the Germans aren't even allowed to speak German in their own schools there. What can you expect? The Versailles Treaty deprived us of our colonies and reduced the size of our country. We shall never be in a

---

Youth leader of the Reich.

position to feed our people. Well, in what direction can we expand? Eastward, into the empty territory of the east. The most natural thing in the world."

"Oh Werner, those are just fatuous phrases. When you come right down to it, it means war."

"Nonsense, the Führer wants peace; he says so in every speech. But the damn Jews are preventing it. Don't you understand that? They have their international connections. They have sworn to destroy Germany. Why? Because we've found them out, also because we're the most industrious nation of the world. You must admit that nobody on earth works as hard as the German. With the Jews we run into hatred, lust for power, money."

But the STUERMER,* you must admit, is nothing but exaggerated trash."

"Klaus," Werner laughed, "the STUERMER is written for the simpleminded; in fact, *by* simple people for the man on the street."

"That's probably true of Streicher."*

"Klaus, the important thing is that basically he's right."

"But Werner, I can't quite see, for example, how the Jews we know can be called subhuman. You met Lilo Simon at our house. She's not an international criminal. Why, she's tops!"

"Naturally, if you pick out a few examples, you can refute everything. But you have to look at the over-all picture. These are facts that researchers have established. Just ask those who have suffered under the Jews."

"Well, of course, my grandfather can't stand them; he lost everything because of the Jews. During the inflation they first bought up his brewery and then declared bankruptcy, while my grandfather was out on his ear. Even his well-earned pension went up in smoke.

"Typical, Klaus, typical. When you think that we are dealing with a group who for centuries never dreamed of giving up their religion, their disgusting slaughter-house customs, their Yiddish and their garlic. They don't work, they bargain; they lend money at exorbitant interest rates; their goal is clear: power through money. By intrigue and trickery they have wormed their way into key positions in finance, the press, culture. In order to achieve their goal they become immoral, unscrupulous and dangerous. The Talmud demands that they despise and exploit Christians. Klaus, if it weren't for our Führer, the Jews would surely be at our throats. But now they can't push us around any more; we're strong

---

*An anti-Jewish smear-sheet.
**The fanatic who published the paper.

enough to expose them and segregate them."

"But making them wear the star of Israel on their coats and all that is so stupid. Lilo can't even come to the swimming pool anymore because she's Jewish."

"Even so, Klaus, the Jews here are better off elsewhere in Europe. Where they are tolerated, most of them live in ghettos and have for centuries. That can't be accidental. At a time like this, when great decisions are being made, there are always a few unfortunate exceptions. In 1918 we were the scapegoats. The big objective, Klaus, is what counts."

And the big objective was gaining momentum. Many found it convenient to blame everything on the Jews. The personal experiences of a few were cited as typical. The venom of individual fanatics whose statements were avidly passed on—worse still, the indifference of the majority was directed against the Jews.

The propaganda machine of Jesuit-trained Joseph Goebbels, Hitler's propaganda minister, was going at full speed. When he talked about the Jews, he reaped increasing hatred from the fanatics and increasing indifference from the average German. "We have more to worry about than a few Jews," people would say. The percentage of Jews was, in fact, small: roughly comparable to that of the Mormons in the U.S.A. Of course, we all knew about the Nürnberg Law. It regulated social intercourse with Jews, classified them, took away their citizenship and, finally, their basic human rights. It was regarded as terribly exaggerated, and we did not really believe it would ever be enforced.

Then came the Kristallnacht. At first, we scoffed at the expression "spontaneous mob action." These were only toughs of the leather-jacket type who raced through the streets on that day in November 1938 and systematically smashed everything that belonged to Jews. What motivated them? In Paris, the German SS diplomat von Rath was murdered by a Jew named Greenspan. Hitler accused the entire Jewish people. Speechless, but curious as well, the citizens shook their heads as they stood by and watched the rowdies. Why did no one raise his voice? Any active interference would have stamped a person publicly as a friend of the Jews. Who dared that risk?

Jews, now became subject to professional restrictions as well. Moreover, they were obliged to pay the government an enormous forfeit in money for the murder of von Rath. Many businesses now put up signs saying that Jews would not be served.

Most of the Jews still remaining in Germany, such as our friend Lilo and her family, sought desperately to emigrate. Present-day statistics in the Jewish Encyclopedia show that before Hitler's accession to power there were 500,000 Jews in Germany and Austria. By 1939, 350,000 of these had emigrated, leaving approximately 150,000 Jews behind among 69,000,000 Germans and Austrians. Most of these lived in the cities of Vienna, Berlin, Breslau, Frankfurt and Cologne. It is therefore not surprising that most Germans were personally acquainted with scarcely more than two families. In my class at school there was only little Regenstein; in the entire school there were perhaps three Jewish students.

From now on, emphasis was placed upon pre-military training in the H.J. Hans and I had little taste for this and sometimes we were gently warned to take more active part, especially in the Sunday events. Hans then reached the age of eighteen and left the H.J. He was immediately asked whether he wanted to join the Party, the SA or the SS. He said no to all of them and was left in peace. The SS, incidentally, was often rather exclusive. There were the SS horsemen and the SS motorized group, consisting of riding clubs and auto clubs. The SS uniforms were dashing. The members were all volunteers; they had to be six feet tall, in perfect physical condition, pure Aryan of course, of good character and without a penal record. Nevertheless, few among our acquaintances were interested, probably because it was rumored that certain SS units were connected with the concentration camps and that the dread Gestapo was a unit of the SS. Who coming from well-ordered bourgeois circumstances would want to join that sort of organization! The names of Dachau, Theresienstadt, Oranienbaum had now become everyday language to even the most indifferent. Everyone knew that they were camps in which the complainers, the know-it-alls, the traitors, spies, saboteurs, anarchists and Communists landed. "Serves them right," people said. "Anyone who deserts his country in its hour of need must be kept under lock and key." The fact that it was more than lock and key was not exactly clear.

Our military obligations were as follows: At the age of eighteen one was inducted into the Arbeitsdienst or labor service. For half a year every German youth was supposed to become acquainted with physical labor. The projects consisted of public works: dike-building, forest-clearing, canalization, swamp drainage and so on. This was followed by three years of military service. I had the choice of staying at the Gymnasium and hoping that I would not be inducted before my final examination, the so-called Abitur. Or else I could leave school immediately, work in a textile factory for a year, attend a technical school and hope that I would not be drafted before I graduated as a textile engineer. I chose the latter course, chiefly because I now hated school. The teachers were strict, our assignments tremendous, and we found it almost impossible to keep up with the high standards. Mother bought us a small motorcycle, and when Hans was drafted into the Arbeitsdienst, I started my technical training in a small textile mill in Cologne.

Suddenly, we heard that Hitler had signed a treaty with his archenemy, Stalin. Not a soul believed in the probity of either partner.

The outbreak of the war with Poland in September '39 struck me like a bolt out of the blue, but others had long expected it. The general attitude ranged from depressive to reserved and, as Mother said, not in any way comparable to the enthusiasm of 1914. We held our breath as we waited to see what England's stand would be. People seemed to think that the war with Poland would soon be over and that then everything would be back to normal. True, it was soon over, but nothing was normal. The English and French must have been mad to help those lousy Poles and declare war on us. Damn it all! Once again everybody was against us.

We sat glued to our radios and proudly listened to the special bulletins announcing the victory of our armies. Then came the first air-raid alarm. The willingness of the people to help in the air defense, the zeal of the army, of the home front and the armament industry was without precedent.

I now commuted every day from Cologne to Wuppertal where I attended the textile school. Across the street from it was an art school where we soon made friends with the students. One of them was the Dutchman, Jim, an amusing type, full of humor, sarcasm and often bitter criticism. One day he disappeared; no one knew what had happened to him. Six months later my friend Walter ran into him and he was on his way to collect his belongings and to depart for Holland. Walter scarcely recognized him. His artist's hands were broken and crippled. He had turned gray and old, refused to see anyone and said not a word about what had happened. He disappeared forever and we lost a friend whose story we should have believed, whose report might have rescued some of us from our warped outlook. Instead, we were left with vague forebodings which took root in our hearts and made us tense, critical and cautious. At one time we would have said: "If only the Führer knew about this!" Now the expression became almost ironical. Even though we believed that all too many of his underlings had failed miserably, nevertheless, it was clear that Hitler mapped out the general strategy. And yet—the time had not come for us to criticize him personally. Things would have to get much worse before that happened. And so they did.

Before I go on with this account of what happened in Germany during the Hitler era, I must answer a question that I am frequently asked: Wasn't life terribly monotonous under the constant pressure, hopelessly dull and drab? Not at all. I was young and wanted to enjoy my youth before the army got hold of me. And we did enjoy it as best we could. We had a marvelous time at the textile school where there was a surplus of girls. Though everything else was rationed, wit, love, wine and song were available to all. Life goes on, even under despots. Girls can look chic even in cheap dresses, red lips are meant to be kissed and soldiers on leave are not interested in politics. No matter how opposed one is to power, when a friend comes home from the front, one listens spellbound to his experiences. War makes life more dangerous, but other things happen that the average worthy citizen scarecely dreams of. Shifting circumstances also caused families and friends from all parts of Germany to move to other areas. In this way they became acquainted with all kinds of people and their customs. From a cultural standpoint everything imaginable was being offered. In art and architecture a trend toward neo-realism with classical overtones was favored. Monumental paintings and massiveness in every form were the order of the day. Actually, the effect was monotonous and boring but we were offered too much art of all ages to care one way or another about the new trend. As for political pressure, I was, as I have said, not politically-minded. Whatever the government decreed was accepted as fact. Obedience and loyalty toward authorities were taken for granted. Hence a person who was not looking for trouble did not need to fear pressure from above. Once the war was on and more and more mistakes were uncovered, it was too late for anyone who valued his life and his freedom to do anything about them. Every sort of criticism was not seen from the standpoint of the crisis; everyone who thought differently had to figure on being condemned as a traitor. Thus, while our armies occupied France, Belgium, Holland, Denmark and Norway, I was spending the happy days of a student who, as cock of the walk, flirts from one amorous adventure to another.

My friend, Walter Brockhaus, was appointed student leader, an appointment which we regarded as a huge joke, since he was anything but a Nazi leader. For many new students this post proved a blessing. As I have said, no one was pressured into joining the HJ, but everyone who wished to study was obliged to have the O.K. of the local student leaders, without which no university or technical school dared admit a student. The student leader demanded certification from the HJ that a candidate had spent at least four years in that organization. In my case a number of strings were pulled, and there was much running back and forth before I received certification, for I had taken little active part in the last few years. Walter, of course, was utterly lenient and certified everyone.

It was 1941. The air war was raging and every other night there were alarms and raids. The news of Hess's flight to England was received with bated breath. Somehow, we hoped that he would be able to initiate negotiations which would eliminate England from the war. He did not and after this incident the hate propaganda against England was intensified.

During the school holidays we volunteered to work in an armament factory. The much-touted mobilization proved so senseless that we lost all enthusiasm. However, the work in these factories continued without interruption. Night after night, demoralized by air alarms, inadequately fed, the workers on the home front suffered no less than the soldiers on the battlefield. We were ashamed not to be able to be more effective.

Letters from my brother seemed to point to the inevitableness of war with the Soviet Union. His unit was suddenly transferred to the Russian border. In every letter he regretted having landed with the infantry. My age group was now in line for induction. I hoped I would still be able to take my final examination before I was drafted. Though my entire course of study could not be taken seriously, nonetheless it gave me a foundation for a subsequent profession. But, more important, I had done something with my youth; I had tasted the wonder of first love and had made a few lasting friendships.

At home Mother's life was becoming lonely. The big house was a burden. Coal was growing scarce; it became impossible to heat the house all winter long; Mother was obliged to let the furnace go out and relight it practically every day. My motorcycle stood jacked up in the garage. Gasoline was rationed. Mother volunteered as an air warden and apprehensively awaited the day when I, too, would leave her to go to war. The war was going successfully for us—except for the air attacks—except for the d--d Party bigwigs who were living well at home—except for that business with the Cologne Jews who were all sent away. Poor Lilo! Where might she be? Yes, and except for K.R. Kreiten, the marvelous pianist and our fellow-student at the Gymnasium, who was simply shot—because of defeatism, so it was said. Good Lord! if one thought about it, there was so much wrong, indeed criminal. But be careful about using hard words! Once the war is over these things will be straightened out.

And then it all began with Russia. Our initial success was quite overwhelming. Entire enemy divisions were captured and thousands of tanks were annihilated. "How lucky that Hitler did not wait for this attacking army to overrun us," people said. Special bulletins came thick and fast, and it looked as though we would be in Moscow before the year was up. I was beginning to feel uncomfortable as a civilian. Most of my schoolmates were inducted before their final examinations. I had the feeling that people were pointing at me and saying: "Why is this young chap still around while all the others are soldiers?" Perhaps I won't be called up for the Arbeitsdienst. Let's hope it won't be the infantry.

Chapter Two
1942

"Workers! Each of you is about to enter a new phase of your life. From now on you will serve your country directly. The purpose of your training with us will be first of all to make you mentally and physically fit and thus prepare you for your subsequent military training. Secondly, you are to learn hard physical work, how to respect it and carry it out wherever you are needed, at home or at the front. Thirdly, you will learn to live in a community and respect communal life. It will weld you together in good and bad times, and you will realize that the human being is capable of functioning only within the framework of organized society. Our German people are a social unit. The German Reich is our home, our destiny. The Führer is our model."

"Attention! Our Fuhrer and Chancellor, the guarantor of certain victory, Adolf Hitler. Victory, Heil!"

Oberfeldmeister Menke stretched out his arm and shouted "Victory" three times. The answering threefold "Heil" was rather feeble. He dropped his arm abruptly and, pulling his well-tailored uniform jacket straight, he looked back to another officer who was standing diagonally behind him, turned around quickly and, with a rapid, almost capering step, walked over to the officers' barracks.

"I am Obertruppführer Schubert and should be addressed as such," said the man. "We members of the Arbeitsdienst lost the title 'Mr.' between 1918 and 1939. We leave that form of address to officers or students." He spoke very softly, almost threateningly and the 150 new workers scarcely dared breathe. He was young and good-looking with dark hair and deep-set penetrating eyes that were somewhat too close together. When he said "students" his lips parted in a revolting sneer. "As head of the Arbeitsdienst, I shall take over the command today. At ease!"

I looked back across the bleak, muddy courtyard toward the gray barracks that were badly in need of paint. In the middle of the yard stood the flagpole from which hung the red swastika flag in limp, wet folds. The fog was so thick that I wasn't sure whether it was drizzling or just damp.

Here and there I heard coughing and throat-clearing. While Schubert was dividing the men into groups, some of them were trying to form their own units. This caused a certain confusion and suddenly Schubert yelled: "Halt!" His face was an angry grimace. He was introducing us to respect, obedience and all the more or less necessary folderol that everyone in uniform mutely accepts.

The camp had not been made ready for our arrival. Our uniforms weren't expected for three days. We sent home special delivery letters for knives, forks and spoons, soap, towels, toothpaste, shoe cream and so on. The few officers there had but recently returned from Russia and did not feel like immediately starting in on us civilians. Moreover, it was rumored that our age group, 1923, would shortly be transferred into the armed forces. There were not enough auxiliary officers. The food was miserable and our state of mind, like the weather, was lousy. As I lay on my straw pallet the first night and thought things over, I was not dissatisfied. I had not expected anything better and was quite prepared for long years of military service. I was determined to do my best and to get through this period as honorably as possble.

Just before I fell alseep I had a strange thought. I suddenly remembered a recurrent childhood dream in which I imagined that I was really the son of a very important man. Everybody knew this, but nobody mentioned it, probably so that I should not become arrogant. But I knew that nothing bad could happen to me; if things became too difficult, the game would be up and I would suddenly find myself back in the role that was really meant for me. As I thought of this dream and listened to the sound of taps outside, I had the strange feeling that I was not really experiencing all this, but just observing it. And this was the feeling I henceforth carried with me like a talisman: I'm not really participating; I'm here just to observe.

"Dreihof, Palatinate   Camp RAD* 4/310

February 1942

Dear Mother:

Please sign the enclosed prescribed form extending my Arbeitsdienst beyond the normal period. Perhaps I was a bit too snappy and they decided to make me an auxiliary Führer for the age group that is next in

---

*Reichsarbeitsdienst.

line. They can retain four men in each company as auxiliary Führers. If I don't do it voluntarily, with your signature, they can still keep me here, but that lessens my chances of advancement. My age group will be transferred to the armed forces. Incidentally, I am getting leave for my examination. Love to all.

Your Klaus."

Seeing all my friends at school again now that I was in uniform gave me a strange sensation. I felt horribly uncomfortable with my short haircut and the not very attractive uniform. I was treated with particular deference at the exam. At the age of eighteen I was probably the youngest textile engineer. I was relieved when it was all over and I was back on the train. My civilian life was finished; farewells were superfluous. The feeling I had had of being a civilian when others were serving the flag now gave way to increased self-confidence mixed with an awareness of new, interesting, indeed dangerous, things that were awaiting me.

In Dreihof there were changes. While the 1923 group were still training with pick and shovel in peace-time work techniques, the newlyarrived 1924 group received only pre-military training. We were given carbines and gas masks. The brown steel helmet replaced the cap with the A-crease which nobody cared for anyway.

The four of us who were chosen from our company were good friends and felt like old hands among the new men. Jung and Bongarts were auxiliary instructors like myself. Krott became medical assistant and Schäfer was kitchen orderly. My birthday on April 9th was memorable. The four of us celebrated in Krott's infirmary, drank Schäfer's cooking rum out of cups while a first-class zither player provided background music. Never again have I been as drunk as on that night; for years afterwards even the thought of rum made me shudder.

The next morning, shortly before the appearance of the Arbeitsführer, in the midst of roll call, I fell flat on my face unconscious. Two hours later there was another roll call and something special seemed to be brewing. General Maurer was a rare visitor at our camp. We were assembled in the mess hall, and a special roll call was scheduled to take place after the meal. At the officers' table in front of us three high-ranking SS Führers were introduced. Nobody could figure out what they were doing here.

Our steaming plates were on the tables. Nobody spoke. Maurer got up and in a loud voice that sounded like a command said: "Toast!"

"What the hell, it's not up to me," everybody probably thought; "somebody'll be prepared and volunteer." Far from it. The silence was painful. Then I saw Schubert turn his head, fix me with his serpent's eyes and his: "Worker Heck," loud enough so that everyone could hear. I must have turned pale with rage and helplessness. What was the idea, why did Schubert do this? Then I heard myself speak. God knows how I happened to think of the Baldur von Schierach verse:

Some live to fill their bellies full,
They sit before a steaming pot,
They harvest where they have not sown,
While others reap the soldier's lot.

Some spend their days on beds of ease;
In Flander's fields the others lie;
Some spill their blood for others' weal,
Are they alike 'neath heaven's eye?

Maurer's facial expression changed with each line, from rigid to questioning to amiable. Now he grinned at me benevolently and said *"Mahlzeit?"** whereupon Schafer's pea soup had its big moment.

Schubert's eyes kept coming back to me. It was obvious that he hadn't digested my verse altogether, later, it occurred to me that he might have read another meaning into it, which made me smile. Across the table Schubert hissed: "Heck, stop your silly grinning."

After the meal there was oppressive silence. Maurer introduced the three SS men and said they had an important announcement to make. All three were handsome, correct, grave, upright and self-confident. They all wore the knight's cross.*** Their gray field uniforms with the little bird on the left sleeve were well tailored. What they had to say was a paean for the Waffen SS.** They spoke of the German ideal of duty and the joy of duty, of the meaning of the war, the hardship, the fighting. At this juncture each of them pointed out how much more of everything the men in the Waffen SS had. They appealed to us to volunteer for the Waffen SS, and they certainly did their best to show us its special advantages compared to other branches of the military. They described their fighting experiences without speaking too much about themselves, and most of the members of the Arbeitsdienst undoubtedly regarded them as heroes.

When the last one had finished, we sat there silently like sheepish school children who had just heard their principal scold other students. I thought it was over now and was about to breathe a sigh of relief when the senior SS man stood up again and said: "I should like all those to rise who have decided to volunteer for the SS!"

So that was it—from onlookers we had become participants. They expected a decision. Again I felt like a school boy: I had not memorized my vocabulary and the teacher is asking for it. Nobody looks him in the eye for fear of being called upon. Just as in school, we clear out throats, something is dropped on the floor. The question hangs in the air and we look around. Slowly but surely we all realize that no one is getting up. Is it

---

*A customary expression to wish one's tablemates an enjoyable meal.
**A military service organization.
***Highly respected war decoration.

possible? Not one among 150? In a way, I'm hoping someone will, just to put an end to this ordeal. The SS man looks incredulous and says: "Perhaps you did not understand me. I repeat..." Then Reister on the rear bench gets up. Heavens, anyone but him. He's crazy—ridiculous. Everybody stares at him and suddenly burst out laughing. Reister is the camp's blockhead, an utter nincompoop and an unfortunate figure from the very first day.

General Maurer comes forward, calls for quiet, exchanges a few words with the SS men and says: "Everyone except the first platoon dismissed!"

As the others filed out, we look at each other in dismay. Then the man next to me remarked that the SS height is six feet, and the first platoon are the tallest men. Schubert, leader of the first platoon, made us line up according to height. I was the third. Before we knew what was happening to us, the three SS men approached us. Schubert had stepped behind me and I felt his eyes in the back of my neck. One of the SS officers had a notebook in his hand, and the three of them were already standing before the first man.

"Why do you not wish to volunteer for the SS?" I heard the question and my brain began to work furiously.

"I have already volunteered for the air force," was the sharp, clear and somewhat too loud reply.

The SS officer did not bat an eye. The one with the notebook did not write anything down, and the same question was asked of the second man in line. The answer was like a pistol shot: "I have volunteered for the navy."

Seconds had gone by and I had no time left to think up an answer before they had moved on to me and put the question to me. And once again my answer came so fast that later I often wondered about it. "I am planning to join the traditional regiment of my father."

"Explain yourself!"

"My father and my grandfather were officers in the 55th cavalry regiment. It was the wish of my deceased father that I carry on this tradition and enlist as a cadet in the 55th cavalry regiment when I'm of age for military service."

The senior SS officer stood with his arms akimbo and rocked back and forth on his heels. "Did you ever hear of a cavalry regiment in this war?" he asked, addressing the question partly to me, partly to his colleagues. The second SS officer laughed, but the third leaned toward the questioner and whispered something into his ear. He, in turn, looked at me and apparently expected an answer.

"The 55th cavalry regiment made an excellent showing in the Polish campaign as well as in France, and was mentioned in the military report."

My voice became a bit shaky and I was close to tears, which probably gave the impression of wounded pride. Actually, it was sheer terror. The cup passed from me and the three officers moved along to my neighbor on the left. From that moment on I heard and saw nothing; all that kept going round my head was: "Let's hope they don't find out." My explanation had been nothing but an excuse. My grandfather had never even been a soldier and my father was an artillery man. I had said cavalry merely to make the idea of tradition more plausible.

In the evening, after hours, an orderly came to my room and requested me to go see Obertruppführer Schubert in his quarters.

Schubert's barracks apartment was Spartan. Fastidiously clean and neat, with very few personal things, it differed from our quarters only in that it was meant for a single occupant, had curtains, a radio and a bookcase. When I entered, Schubert asked me to sit down, to relax and forget that he was my superior officer. He wanted to speak to me privately. I felt slightly uncomfortable, as always in Schubert's presence, and decided to be on my guard. I glanced at the bookcase: VOLK OHNE RAUM, VOM ZARENADEL ZUR ROTEN FAHNE, MEIN KAMPF, Rilke, FAUST, a Spanish-German dictionary, a book by Bergengruen. On the wall hung a motto: "Work ennobles."

"Heck," he said, "I'm not sure whether you know that we Arbeitsdienst leaders go over to the Waffen SS when our time comes. At least, that is expected of us. Since I also have private feelings, aside from my official feelings, and am therefore interested in other opinions, I should like to ask you why you did not volunteer for the SS. That traditional regiment nonsense was too obvious to me; I know you too well to have been taken in by it. Now don't think I have anything against you or that I'll use what you say here either for or against you. I'm asking you as Schubert to Heck and want you to give me a straight answer." His manner of speaking was altogether different from the way he gave commands. His sentences were stilted, as though he had rehearsed them, and his voice was so low that I had difficulty understanding him.

I had leaned back and crossed my legs. I took out a cigarette and asked whether he objected. "Your manner and the cigarette in my room show how litttle you have in you of the soldier. We are, after all, soldiers. But, as I said, I want you to talk as a human being, not as a soldier. So go ahead."

I had always been fond of debates and welcomed discussions. In this case, however, I decided that a certain paradox was necessary. "you want candid answers," I said boldly. "I agree, but I must say in advance that when I leave here I shall take my opinion with me. If anything is ever said about our private conversation, I shall reserve the right to deny that we ever had this talk. And now to your question. In school we were once discussing a short story by Bergengruen. It was about the daughter of a count who fell in love with the son of a hangman. The boy did not reveal his origin to her. When the count learned of it, he was beside himself. He told his daughter the truth and she was now obliged to let her heart decide for her. I've forgotton how the story turned out, but that is unimportant. Our German teacher made a sort of sociological study out of it. He described the young man's good sides, said that his father's profession had been handed down from one generation to the next, that his home life was respectable. The girl was spoiled, but sensitive, honest and warmhearted. Our teacher then asked us whether ideas in our more enlightened and classless society were different and asked those to raise their hands who would nowadays still be in favor of breaking off such a relationship. He did not expect anybody to raise his hand, but my friend Peter Rubach and I did so spontaneously. We were the only ones. Everybody laughed, called us snobs and old-fashioned."

I paused and lit my cigarete. Schubert was leaning forward; he kept looking at my fingers and coughing nervously.

"My answer is the same today. Of course, I see the necessity of justice. People are needed whose duty is to mete out punishment. But it seems to me this is a necessary evil of our society, of any society. I've never liked policemen and have no desire to meet hangmen. I reserve the right to avoid such people. If I should discover these facts too late, I should feel that my trust had been misused. Trust is the basis of love. Therefore the Bergengruen story could not have had a happy ending."

"And what about the SS?" asked Schubert.

"The facts are known."

"Do you mean to say that the SS men who do their duty are hangmen?" Schubert asked wide-eyed.

"I am saying that they are given special orders to carry out punishments, to guard concentration camps, to undertake retaliatory measures."

"Aren't these measures necessary? Aren't they within the framework of the law? Doesn't all this benefit you too?"

"Who am I to judge? All I know is that for this reason I shall never volunteer for the SS."

"Hm, those are strong words. Well, I told you, this was a private conversation. My personal opinion is that you had the wrong friends. What's this friend Peter doing?"

"Peter has already been killed, as an infantryman, in the attack on Osel."

"Hm, I could say something cynical, but I won't. All right, Heck; it was interesting. Forget it. Good night."

Our duties were strenuous. Besides the musketry training and the

Arbeitsdienst program, we were given bicycles. We pedaled three abreast in long columns, to the amazement of the civilian population. Our trips through vast stretches of the Palatinate were feats of endurance. As foreman, I had neither shovel, spade nor hoe on my bicycle. My modest post paid additional dividends: I had a mattress bed, and even when I went out occasionally, the little stripe on my collar gave me advantages. I succeeded in attracting the attention of an innkeeper's daughter, an achievement that earned me the respect, envy, hatred, whatnot, of my men.

The air war at home assumed threatening proportions. News from my brother on the eastern front was alarming. However, spring was in the air, and the fronts would soon be on the move again; new victories seemed imminent. Who knows, I thought, perhaps the war will soon end successfully and I not even be in it. Our training lasted till the early part of May—until then the dullness of barracks life, the physical labor, the drill, the bicycle marathons continued.

Then suddenly came the order to load up. On the small platform in Dreihof stood an empty freight train, and before we knew it we were waving goodbye to a few onlookers. My little friend had come with two thick sandwiches for me, and the men teased her because of the tears. I was rather astonished and bewildered by them, but decided that they bolstered my ego.

We rolled along for sixteen days and nights, sometimes for short distances, then for many hours. Once, we stood still for a whole day, another time we backed up for hours. We were moving in the direction of the rising sun. No one knew our destination. We occupied nothing but cattle cars with two long, straw-filled bunks on either side. I believe there were sixteen men in my car. Our few duties consisted of peeling potatoes, cleaning our rifles, polishing our boots and straps, maintaining order and cleanliness. The rest was pure gravy. Now and then, the train would stop, a whistle would sound and the men detailed to fetch the food would run to the kitchen car and come back with steaming dishes. Every third day I would dash to the locomotive to get hot water for shaving. We sang, laughed and told each other our life stories. Most of the men were from Cologne, and the majority of them had been inducted just before the Abitur. They came from respectable families. For most of us the dark side of life was limited to the recent bomb terror, the endless air alarms, the fact that sweets were getting scarce. Suffering, hunger, despair were unknown to us. Some, like myself, had been exchange students in foreign countries. On the political side, we ranged from the ignorant to the indifferent, with very few exceptions. Most of us had, at one time or another, gone on camping trips, and the songs we sang belonged to a different day and age.

Landsknecht's life, happy life,
In the tavern day and night;
You laugh and sing
Or out you go,
We're naught but jolly fellows.

It was all quite romantic and we loved to think of ourselves in the role of landsknechts.

The landscape and the climate changed from spring to summer. There were fewer villages to be seen and the country became flat and lonely. The station signs were no longer in German. It took us some time before we realized that we were in Poland. Once, the train stopped in the middle of nowhere. We were just peeling potatoes. A little boy of about ten dashed out of a nearby shack and came running over to us. Dirty and illkept, in ragged clothing, he stood panting beside our car. He looked at us and called out a few words. He was the first Pole we were to see. We laughed and replied with a few nonsense words such as *dobshe, dobsche, tralala*. Then from the rear of our car a few remnants of buttered bread and sausage rind came sailing out and landed at his bare feet. Greedily he stuffed everything into his mouth. We gazed at him as at an animal in the zoo. We quickly decided that the boy was feebleminded. Somebody said: "Poland, nix culture," and we shook our heads. When one of the men swept out our potato peels, the boy gathered them all up, stuffed them into his ragged shirt and ran off. Our train started moving again.

Now and then a few dilapidated or demolished farms came into view. When we drew into the dismal station at Brest, one man who seemed to know something about history said: "This is where Russia begins." Our spirits became somewhat more subdued, and we spoke of our brothers and friends who were fighting in this country. We were evidently on our way to the front. We now had a few cars up ahead with soldiers and aircraft arms, and this gave us a rather tingling sensation. Apparantly, some kind of attack was expected. Then there were rumors of partisan bands who were shutting off supply routes.

One foggy morning, the train stopped again on an open stretch. We slid open the big door. Swamp. Suddenly we all came to life. Look, those are women working there. We stuck our heads out. Sure enough, at the end of our car a ragged figure was swinging a pick on another track. We were scolding and ridiculing the Russians for letting women do such work, when the figure suddenly looked up and, to our astonishment, said in German: "You needn't laugh. I understand you well. I am a German, too, from Berlin, Spandau. But I am a Jew and that was my undoing." The final words she shouted, almost in tears. Nobody said anything. Everybody stared at her. She was young and pretty. A soldier in a German uniform with strange insignia and a Russian cap whistled at her and, waving his rifle, motioned to her to step back from the train. We were thunderstruck. I thought of Lilo Simon, my brother's friend in Cologne. I knew the fate of her family up to the day, shortly before my induction, when all the Jews of Cologne were suddenly spirited away under cover of darkness, to be settled somewhere in the east until the end of the war—for purposes of better supervision, we were told. Lilo was a manicurist, and I pictured her with beautifully groomed hands swinging a hoe. Her visa number for the U.S.A., which she had so desperately awaited had not arrived in time. Oh, why was that necessary!

One man said: "Why should we care about the damn Jews. They're to blame for everything."

"Idiot," said another.

Then there were a few harsh words.

Jung got up and imitated Goebbel's nasal voice: "Everyone of our countrymen says he knows at least one decent Jew. With our fifty million Germans, that make fifty million decent Jews. I ask you, my German countrymen, where do all these Jews come from?" Everybody laughed and the train moved on.

The swamp seemed endless. Once there was a long wait. From the front of the train the news filtered through that the tracks had been blasted and were being repaired. Towards evening and twice during the night we heard rifle shots.

"Buy yourselves combs, boys, we're heading for lousy times!" Jung had a wisecrack for every occasion.

The incident with the Jewish girl kept me awake for a long time, and the ragged little boy, too, kept reappearing as I drifted off. The puffing and rattling of the train finally lulled me to sleep.

We had grown so accustomed to our gypsy life that we were almost disappointed when we were told that we had reached our destination. The name of the little village was Kalinkovitchi. The station wasn't much and the region looked like one of those lousy troop training areas. Our company was now lined up by the Führer of my platoon, Unterfeldmeister Nilius, a short, snappy, well-meaning chap who seemed fair-minded and popular. Schubert had already been transferred to some other post. Every man had his bicycle, half a tent strip as a shelter, blanket, gas mask, rifle and small rucksack. Tools were distributed, and hoes, spades and shovels were fastened to the bicycles. We wore our warm uniforms. With our steel helmets on our belt and all our other paraphernalia, we felt like pack mules. The company had three new trucks: cook truck with food supplies; repair truck with the paperwork of the war; as well as medical assistants, medicines and bandages.

After being given a brief talk, we knew what we were in for. From here we were to cycle in the direction of the front. We were trailing in a long line, one behind the other. At the end came the three trucks. If a man was obliged to stop, a second man had always remained with him. During the rest stops everyone who had fallen behind was to find his way back to his unit. And off we went!

At first, theory and practice diverged but slightly; later on, increasingly so. It was warm, too warm for our uniforms, and we suffered in silence until the command came: "Top buttons open." We regarded this as a huge joke and thereafter the top button was never closed. Moreover, we rolled the sleeves of our uniforms up over the garish swastika bands. Dust filtered into everything, and after only a few miles on the sandy road we were encrusted, thirsty, soaked with sweat, tired and miserable.

There were said to be partisans in the region. Good, let them come and introduce themselves. The idea of sending scouts ahead on either side of the road was simply abandoned. We had detrained in the middle of the Rokitno swamp area. We soon reached the town of Rjetchitza and puffed our way eastward. The road was a dam, twenty meters wide, sandy, with deep wagon tracks. Where the sand was soft, cycling was torture; where it was packed down, we made good headway. There was swampy woodland on either side. One step to the side and we stood up to our knees in swamp. There were swarms of gnats, and bullfrogs croaked day and night. Rjetchitza was a poor little village. Inquisitively the peasants came out into the street and gazed at us. We made our first stop. The cook truck came along and we had a wonderful meal. We pitched our tents on the edge of the village. Thus, the curtain was rising on the second act of our nomadic life.

At six o'clock the next morning we were on our way again. Our column stretched out in a long line in the sun and sand. The countryside was always the same: endless road and swamp. Once, an aged Gorki type came toward us, ragged, with a long beard, a sack of roots and herbs slung over his shoulder. A wanderer from where? Going where?

Two hours later, a rifle shot. A hundred yards ahead a man fell off his bicycle. Hallermann, dead, shot through the head. We were paralyzed with shock. Nobody knew where the shot came from. We stared into the swamp and the croaking frogs seemed to be mocking at us. Nilius stayed with the body. We had to push on. Toward evening, a second shot. Five minutes later the message was shouted forward in relays: another dead in the second platoon. So these were the partisans. There wasn't a thing we could do.

But even the partisans must eat and sleep. They could be everywhere and nowhere. At first we suspected the lonely wanderers who passed us now and then. We searched them and found nothing. If we came to the villages, we combed them thoroughly. Once, we found parts of uniforms; another time, a concealed, unusable automatic pistol. The people were intimidated and must have regarded us as superior Party officers with our grayish brown uniforms and swastika armbands. We found nothing that would have justified taking any action. The second night we spent in Gomel, in an old barn. We were too tired to look around in the town. A few crumbling churches were used by the Russians as garages for tractors, and the universal poverty seemed genuine and depressing. We were roused at three in the morning. For a week already the sun had risen at our left. We cycled south and reached Tchernigov.

We were now in North Ukraine and the difference was notable. The villages looked far more inviting. The inhabitants waved to us cheerfully, with flowers in their hands. Great barter transactions were conducted: sweetening tablets were exchanged for eggs. Here in Tchernigov we came across Rumanian officers being trained under German supervision. Mounted, in elegant uniforms, they struck us as rather operatic figures. The landscape became hilly and sometimes reminded me of the Odenwald. The partisan nightmare ended, only to give way to other calamities. Sand fleas bit our legs, and everybody was covered with sores. Then we developed regular epidemics of carbuncles on our necks. Three times the back of my neck was lanced and smeared with ichthyol. Some men ran temperatures. Dutifully we swallowed our daily, bitter, yellow malaria pills. To top it all, we had body lice. Anybody examining us more closely would no longer have mistaken us for "elite." Dusty, itching, our eyes bloodshot, our necks and legs swathed in bandages, our feet steaming in padded shoes, thirsty, afraid of village springs that were said to be polluted; irritated because we knew not where we were going nor why, we continued doggedly cycling eastward until, utterly exhausted, we reached Krolovik. The last five kilometers we not only had to push our bicycles but virtually carry them; the rain that had suddenly set in turned the road into a sea of mire and our bicycle wheels into lumps of mud.

However, Krolovik made up for everything. First of all, we were quartered in a schoolhouse where we discovered German textbooks. Then we had four days of rest, which helped straighten out all our kinks. One evening, we were invited to the community hall by the village eldest. It was rumored that a theatrical performance was to take place. We dressed up and put fresh gauze bandages on our sore necks. Members of the Kiev National Theatre, who had sought refuge here, gave us a firstclass performance of scenes from operas and operettas. We were enthusiastic.

The next evening there was a terrific hullabaloo. We were sitting outside the schoolhouse drinking an extra ration of liquor when, out of the clear sky, fifty or sixty chaps on small horses thundered into the yard. We couldn't believe our eyes. Carrying crooked sabers and pistols clad in

Cossack caps, Russian boots and German uniforms with strange insignia on their sleeves, they raised a vast cloud of dust. Within seconds they were surrounded by women and children. It took a while before the dust settled and our interpreter had the story straight. They were Cossacks, a hundred strong, who had mobilized against the partisan bands. Hordes of them, accompanied by kith and kin, were on the warpath against the Bolsheviks. They were delighted to learn that we had the same objective. Thus, officially they were under the German high command, but they were fighting on their own and had suffered considerable losses. They were a tough, grinning, bandy-legged lot who, that same evening, roasted a lamb on the spit, sang wild songs and tossed their legs into the air when they danced. We bartered cigarettes with them, but our communication was limited to: "Stalin, nix good, Hitler, good. All comrades." Later, they became melancholy, and finally a few Cossack wives wept aloud for their fallen husbands.

Jung, Bongarts and I walked to a nearby hillside and in the bright moonlight we looked toward the east. A few kilometers in that direction the Ukraine came to an end, and beyond that, 100 kilometers as the crow flies, was Kursk and the battlefront. What the devil were we doing here?

As the cross flies indeed! It was 300 kilometers on our bicycles, and no joke. Someone remarked that we were now in the center of the blackearth region. That sounded interesting, but only a cyclist could possibly know what it meant. On roads devoid of stones, that looked velvety soft in the summer wind, that are called roads only because they are wide, on such roads any sort of vehicle, even a lousy bicycle, becomes a sort of sunset. Clouds of dust hung motionless over them, and a kilometer-long row of bicycles, one behind the other, raised much dust as an army corps. When the rain beat down on these roads they became bottomless. Cycling became an abysmal joke. Black-earth country— how well I knew it!

Shortly before we reached Kursk, we struck the main transport route. Finally we saw German *landser** and armored vehicles, and in the general melee we lost five men who did not find their way back to us for two weeks. Ten kilometers southeast of Kursk we halted and assembled in a wooded section where we rested for two days. We had reached the front! It could all have been simpler if our train had shipped us straight to Kursk. However, some top planner must have decided to let us cycle 750 kilometers for four weeks through the Russian hinterland, at the price of two dead, three hospitalized with carbuncles, to say nothing of sweat and tears. But now the only thing was to look ahead. Ahead lay the east.

Slang for common soldier.

Hardships were soon forgotten. We had come into the limelight of world history. Things were going on here!

There was plenty going on everywhere. We were well on the way toward winning the war. Rommel's victories in Africa had been announced and on all fronts the German army was attacking at strategic points. As yet we had no mail from home, but the generally confident mood was sometimes dimmed by reports of *landser* who knew details about air attacks on Cologne.

Rain or shine, our shelter from now on was the small, four-man tent. Here in the woods near Kursk, ten kilometers from the front, our company joined up with a Hungarian unit. The big surprise for us consisted of hot goulash and beans. Honvet cigarettes and a bottle of champagne for every two men. Open fires were prohibited; Russian *rathas* had made a couple of low-flying attacks. In the evening we sat with the Hungarians, between the horses, and tried to communicate. Then came the gypsies, four men with fiddle, bull fiddle and cymbals. They moved from one group to another. Their music was melancholy, but always ended with the rhythmic czardas. A few soldiers wept openly. Now and then, a magnesium light would flare up in the distance, and very occasionally we heard the thunder of cannonade.

The next night there was an alarm. At one o'clock everybody was ready to start off. It was June 28, 1942. At 2:15 A.M. all hell broke loose. First, artillery, then dive bombers, then tanks, then infantry. In the midst of the tumult we stumbled along on our iron steeds. At dawn, always following the advancing front, we crossed the old battleline. Dead horses, shattered wagons, burned-out tanks, and from everywhere single Russians running out of the fields with arms raised in surrender. We were horrified to see the broad Mongolian faces of Kalmucks and Kirghiz, the dead and wounded by the roadside, the Russian women in uniform, gunwomen in leather jackets. We felt like saviors from the West. Then suddenly a couple of terrific detonations. Mines. But strangely, when wounded German privates moaned for help, our knees buckled; the wounded Mongols sat there so mute and hopeless that we could not feel much pity for them.

We advanced rapidly. The scorching sun, the dust, the lice and our carbuncles were soon forgotton: we were hastening toward victory. But stop, what's that? On either side of the road, civilians were moving across the fields in long rows. As we drew nearer, we saw long beards, black caftans, wide-brimmed hats. They were grubbing the earth with sticks. Human mine sweepers. A hundred yards behind them, Hungarian soldiers. The two rows moved along 500 yards and a mine exploded. There was a gap in the column. The cruelty of it was like dust in our throats. We could not talk about it; we had to be careful not to lose contact. The rifles and gas masks were asphyxiating, and the condition of the road demanded our full attention. But the injustice, the senselessness of it kept nagging at us. No matter what these Jews had done, this was utterly insane and could never be justified. Hours later, during the next rest interval, we discussed this incident with Nilius. He promised to report it higher up.

After the rest stop came our first work order; filling road holes. The next day, rain; work assignment: building corduroy roads over mine holes; the mud was incredible. At night, clean laundry was distributed; the lice joyfully switched over. The front was not quickly running away from us.

Once again, we are sent into the sticks and, after another 300 kilometers, we camped beside a river. We were given our first major project: building a wooden bridge, approximately twenty yards long, across the river. The heat had exhausted us and a type of mild dysentery had set in, but the work on the bridge helped us all to recuperate. It proved to be a model construction and took us about eight days from the first shovelful of dirt to the final neat sign announcing to posterity that a maximum load of twenty tons was approved by RAD Company A3-310.

About this time we received our first mail and packages from home. The mood was mixed, for some of the men learned that their houses and families had been bombed.

Our journey continued and soon we would be at the Don, north of Voronesh. Once, rifle fire reached us from a village. We were alone with our first platoon, about thirty men strong. Nilius and Pryfzneck, an Obertruppführer, practically fell over themselves giving us orders. We marched up to the village like seasoned warriors, searched all the houses, took two prisoners and that was that. Well, not quite; Pryfzneck got the Iron Cross, 2nd class, which made him proud and us dubious. Somehow, we thought the iron Cross to be a higher honor.

On August 28th we reached our destination: Malinovska, a tiny hamlet thirty kilometers from the main road, forty kilometers from the nearest large town. Jung, who had a map, proudly announced: "Comrades, we're east of Moscow." The thought did not make us exactly happy. Malinovska had some fifty inhabitants. No German soldier had as yet come this far, and sometimes it seemed to us that the people had not even heard of Stalin. We were at the end of the world-our world. The little village was idyllically situated in an oakwood and had a beautiful lake. Its few houses were whitewashed and covered with straw. Each peasant had the usual cow, five chickens, a dog, no toilet, a huge stove that also served as a bed, and milk in jugs in the cellar niche. The village had a community house with tools, a sauna bath, a medicine man, a bicycle without tires, a non-vicious bulldog, a gramaphone, no radio and tremendous respect for us. Everyone was on his best behavior. We stayed in our tents. The community houses became a kitchen, an office and a storehouse. Krott, the medical assistant, moved in with the medicine man and the two learned from each other. To the medicine man we owed the prompt cure of our carbuncles. We gave the peasants flour in exchange for milk. Our job here was to cut down trees and load bunker wood for the construction of a position.

We were up at six, fell in line clad only in bathing trunks, washed in the lake, sprinted through the woods for half an hour, dressed, had breakfast, then cycled two kilometers to a poplar wood. There we cut wood with handsaws and small axes, dragged it to the roadside and stacked it. In the evening we would sit in front ot our tents and listen to the Russians singing wonderful four-part folksongs to the accompaniment of the balalaika and the accordian. Sometimes at night a low-flying Russian gyroplane would slowly approach. Then we would put out all the lights, even our cigarettes and curse Goering because there was no sign of his air force.

The front had come to a halt at the Don, and now moved along south of us toward Stalingrad. It was now September and we were still in Malinovska, still in the Arbeitsdienst in which we were actually supposed to serve only six months. Perhaps we've been forgotton? Autumn arrived and it grew cold. We dug holes three feet deep under our tents, filled them with straw and kept our lice-infested uniforms on all night.

Then we were ordered to load wood. Our trucks were put in shape, and the wood was driven eight kilometers to a railroad loading station. The name of the station was Isbitze, a lonely flagstation in the midle of an endless steppe. The single track was flanked by a small loading ramp and two unused sidings. As head of my group, I had a pleasant life. I had no tools on my bicycle and I bossed the job. A situation like this, however, also had its disadvantages, for it bred envy, if not ill-will. Moreover, when it was cold and everybody kept warm by working, one stood around blowing his nose and shivering. In the woods I was sometimes able to pick up a saw without attracting the attention of any of the Führers. But loading was different. My group had to do the shunting; when one car was full it was maneuvered over the switch onto the main track where it was stopped with a brake log and then pushed over the same switch to the right siding. In other words, we had no locomotive, and since the loading ramp was very small, we kept pushing cars back and forth all day long. The rest of the men loaded wood on trucks, brought it over from the edge of the wood to the cars and loaded. Only twice a train came along the main track. The first time it was an odd-looking truck with a special substructure for use on tracks. Although we waved and would have loved to talk to someone for a change, the unresponsive *landsers** on board

---

Common expression for German soldier.

rattled past. We had no idea where the line led to. Nobody could understand the signal man, and the boy who evidently lived with him scarcely ventured out of the poor little hut. Every third day our train would be picked up by a locomotive. Loading took place once a month.

The second occasion on which something came along the tracks was far more dramatic. It was a bitter cold October day. The sun shone in a cloudless sky and the air was dry and clear. We could see for many kilometers, but on this snow-covered, endless steppe, one's glance always came back to the tracks that led straight as an arrow into nothingness. The work was fun and kept everybody warm. Although I was not allowed to take part, I kept warm by running around. As I looked over my men, I realized that we were all bursting with health. Our summer cycling was long since forgotten and we were in top form. That is, all except Dahlig who had a bad cough. The least exertion in this icy air would bring on coughing fits. He had had this cough for weeks, and we were beginning to get used to it. Since he ran no temperature and did not want to stay behind in camp, he came along and had this special task of placing the brake log onto the main track. This seemed a happy solution, for Dahlig was an odd ball; he always did the wrong thing and was in everybody's way. He never joked with us, and he worshipped Rilke and Mozart. He had a good voice, but when we asked him to sing for us, he chose songs of Strauss and Hugo Wolf, which were not exactly popular. He was a native of Krefeld, and the only Mennonite I have ever known. Once, we discussed religion, another time politics, and I realized that he was fairly well informed. His criticism was bitter, though cautious. Most of the boys regarded him as a know-it-all and spoil-sport.

On this particular afternoon we went at our work with a vengeance. We already had ten full cars on the right siding. The eleventh was just being pushed over the switch onto the main track. Dahlig was a little too slow for me, so I shouted: "Get going, Dahlig, the brake log!" Dahlig rose, started to cough and, before we knew it, the heavily loaded car was rolling slowly past him. At first we remained calm; all the others were runnning toward it and we were sure it would stop twenty yards or so. Far from it. Once it had gained momentum, fifty men could not have held it back. To our amazement, it kept going faster and we were unable to follow. No one had realized that the track was on a slight incline. The car went on and on and we stared after it, annoyed that we would be obliged to roll it back. After two kilometers it came to a stop in a slight hollow. Three details were sent to push it back when suddenly there was terrific shouting from the station hut. The Russian flagman was bellowing something from the window. His boy came running out with a red flag and cried in German: "A train is coming. A hospital train!" And, waving the flag, he ran like mad in the direction of the car. It was a moment before everybody understood. Impossible! Never had a train come by here. Hospital train? My knees felt shaky and I stared down the track beyond the car into the distance. A tiny shadow on the horizon, then a small cloud, then a thin, perpendicular banner of smoke. Everybody yelled, everybody ran, with the boy in the lead, in the direction of the single car. For God's sake, how can we signal the train? the engineer is bound to see the car. But, who knows, perhaps he's not looking out of the window. My responsibility, hospital train-court martial-accident due to neglect! This kept hammering away in my head as I ran through the snow, though I knew it was too late. As the banner of smoke came nearer it changed color. The train slowed down and finally stopped in front of our car, even before our breathless arrival. We all climbed aboard and were pushed back to Isbitze.

It was indeed a hospital train, made up of some twenty coaches. The engineer snarled at us at first, but then he laughed and waved to us in farewell. We were alone again, and I heaved a sigh of relief. Feldmeister Nilius gave me a lecture and then demanded to see Dahlig. Dahlig, where's Dahlig? He had disappeared. Gone. Not a trace. After calling and searching to no avail, we decided he must have gone back to Malinovska. Yet nobody had seen him and it was eight kilometers through snow to Malinovska. We had another four hours of work; then we drove home on our truck. In Malinovska there was not a trace of Dahlig. the next day we organized a search party, but it was fruitless. After three days he was reported missing to headquarters.

About this time came the command to build permanent quarters. We were sunk, for it meant that it would be a long time before we went home; perhaps we would even spend the winter here. Since we had no radio, we depended on the mail for news from the front and from home. Mail was delivered once a week by the supply truck. Our rations varied strangely. Once, we had bread that had been specially packed for Africa; another time, marmalade in tubes, lots of butter and no bread. Sometimes we were even given combat packages of chocolate. Then the soups became thinner and our faces longer.

We built houses for ourselves, excavating them into slopes. they were log constructions with double walls and straw in between. The Russians helped us cover them with straw roofs, and we plastered the sides with mud and cow manure which the Russian girls mixed with their feet. Inside we had wooden benches and a brick stove. Sixteen men to a house; it was almost cozy.

The cold grew so intense that we had to chop holes into the snow and saw blocks of ice out of the frozen lake for wash water. Our work in the woods slowly became torture.

Then it was rumored that we were not going home at all; the infantry would take us over and we would be sent to Stalingrad. Though victory seemed imminent, damn it all, we wanted to go home first. The winter had only begun; but our pep, our good humor had already congealed, our

optimism had vanished with the last warm rays of the sun.

One Sunday morning something was again in the air. It was not hard to guess that it was Sunday, for all the Russians took their sauna baths early in the morning. Later, they sat in their huts and deloused each other's heads. We, strangely enough, had no head lice, but countless body lice. The Führers had a long conference. Then there was a roll call. Oberfeldmeister Mencke came capering up. He went straight to the point and spoke in a loud voice, emphasizing each word: "All come forward who previously volunteered for the SS, the air force or the navy. Also all those who in the mustering were declared fit for the navy or the air force." Dead silence.

"This is important; what's the matter with you, Klaus? Pull yourself together," said a voice within me and, before I knew it, I was standing in front of the company along with nine others. Suddenly, there was snickering. The four of us who had served the longest had all come forward. It must have looked like collusion. "Volunteers in the office! The rest break ranks.!"

Like all offices, this one was overheated, and as we gathered in a semi-circle around the Oberfeldmeister, our faces burned and our uniforms steamed.

"Men," Mencke began, "according to orders from the RAD high command, our company, like all units now in Russia, will within the next few days be absorbed into the armed forces. In order to assure the personnel supply of the SS, the airforce and the navy, we are taking you out now and sending you home. Your statements will be verified. Unterfeldmeister Nilius will leave Malinovska today to fly home by the most direct route. In the district headquarters he will compare the data with the statements you make here. Anyone who is not sure of himself still has a chance to withdraw. If you're caught lying, you'll be answerable to a court martial. Does anyone want to think it over?"

No one stirred. We stood there like duffers. Then we took our turn putting our personal data on paper. I maintained that I had been mustered for the antiaircraft, which was not exactly correct. If worst came to worst, it was a misunderstanding, I argued with myself.

"For God's sake, what nonsense; antiaircraft is not what's meant here. If they say air force, they mean fliers!" The office sergeant gave me a superior smile.

"What you or 'they' mean is unimportant; what's printed here is what counts," I took the liberty of saying-well, wasn't I a rank higher? "The command says 'air force' and antiaircraft is a division of the air force."

When we were outside again and compared notes, we discovered that everybody had looked at it the same way I had.

The rest of the men were furious, depressed, mute, resigned to the inevitable-each according to his nature. The idea of having sacrificed almost a year to the Arbeitsdienst at the age of eighteen and then not even getting a chance to go home on leave, but being taken up into the infantry here in the depth of winter, was certainly depressing for everybody. Of course our own statements did not fool anybody, not even the Führers. Nilius left for home that same day. When he shook my hand in farewell, his gaze lingered on me. I knew he liked me.

Two days later came the order to depart. In a few hours everything was packed and taken in numerous trips to Isbitze. There, a small train stood ready. We said goodbye to the people of Malinovska, swept out our dwellings, bolted the heavy wooden doors and wondered who would be keeping house there after us. The assembled peasants murmured, "Do swidjane. "The men doffed their caps and grinned. We left an address with the village eldest; we could not give up hope of one day hearing something of Dahlig's fate.

The stoves in the cattle cars were soon glowing. I was in the last car. As we started rolling, I opened the door a crack and looked back. The sun was sinking blood-red behind our wood lot. The flagman and his boy were standing together, waving. Soon they were nothing but silhouettes. And now, suddenly, it seemed to me there were three standing there. I was about to call to Jung, when I saw a tiny flash, thought I heard a brief shot. The third figure was no longer there. Was I dreaming? I could have sworn there were three men. Now everything became blurred, the atmosphere was shimmery and the sun was sinking perceptibly. In the distance, Isbitze faded into the night and into the past. I closed the door of the cattle car, went to my straw-filled sleeping sack, crossed my arms in back of my head and heard the men singing. My thoughts were in a turmoil. I thought of home and suddenly remembered something Helmut Weisbach's father said:"If you want to know what's wrong with Germany today, Klaus, just consider what happens to the man who thinks differently in this land of thinkers." Why the devil must I recall that particular statement at this moment?

The trip was short. Llgov was the name of the town where we detrained and were billeted. The very next day everybody except the Führers and the ten of us changed over into military uniforms. The instructors were themselves still in training, so that we continued to remain in charge for a while. That created an unusual situation: an infantry company being led by an RAD foreman on his way to the training ground. The standing joke, of course, was: wait till Nilius gets back; then you'll change over too and silently join our ranks. We did not feel comfortable.

A fortnight later the time came. Nilius returned, immediately called us into the improvised office, gave us a sharp look and grinned. "I had no time for such petty details in Germany. Anyway, we need you as transport command for our RAD belongings.!"

We practically embraced him and said farewell to our men. My last day with them was on a training field in Llgov. In bitter cold, in ice and snow, an attack on a series of positions. It was the last straw!

Bicycle uniforms, tools and our three trucks were loaded on the train. It was like the return of an expedition and, as we rolled westward our hearts grew lighter with every kilometer. Anything but Russia. This year had not brought us victory, and in Stalingrad a smash-up seemed inevitable. What was it my brother had written from the front?" Another winter like this and we're finished for all time. When we rolled into Brest-Litovsk I breathed a sigh of relief. Russia was behind us; I had done what was expected of me.

> "R.A.D. Supreme Commander, Hx1 at Army High Command, November 6, 1942.

> Certificate. Obervormann Klaus Heck returning from his recent commitment in the zone of operations of the Army High Command, on his way to service at the home front. He is entitled to receive a furlough package at the border checkpoint.

> RAD Supreme Commander   Stamp   Furlough package. Führer gift."

Everyone received this form and we waited in the train until our turn came to leap over the tracks and accept our packages in the station barracks. It was bitter cold and merciless wind whistled through the cracks of our cars. The little stove glowed and smoked. Our eyes smarted. Slowly a freight train moved between us and the barracks. Hot steam hissed from the locomotive and for a moment we were enveloped in a dense fog. The train was heading east, in the opposite direction, and stopped in front of us. Cattle cars, like ours. Then I heard Nilius whistle. Hurry, it's our turn. Damn it, now we have to crawl under the other train or climb between the cars. The locomotive was being uncoupled. A few minutes later, we all returned with our packages.

Gosh, what a stink. Where in the world is that latrine smell coming from? Somebody pointed to Jung's back. We examined each other more closely: every second man had the stuff on his uniform and cap. Bongarts was the first to size up the situation. He climbed out of the car and pointed to the lower part of the cars that stood beside us on the adjoining tracks. We all got out and, to our horror, saw human excrement dripping through the wooden floors into the dirty snow. Then we discovered that the small windows in the corner of each car were barred. Here and there was even a face with a ghastly expression gazing out at us. We looked down the length of the ghost train. There we saw two double sentries clad in uniforms that were half Russian, half German, carrying rifles over their shoulders.

"What sort of train is that? Who's in it?"

"*Nje pagne mai.*"

Richter spoke a little Polish. He was told: "Sick Russian war prisoners."

But for Christ's sake, who's out of his mind here? Sick Russian war prisoners, a whole trainload, and what a train! And here in Brest, traveling eastward? Well, that's the end. I'm going to write and tell Hitler about this. There's somebody here who's fouling things up. If the Führer knew that! I went to Nilius who had already found out about it. His lips were a thin line, as always when he was angry. At that moment our cars clanked together, the whislte sounded and the train started up.

Nilius, the snappy little chap with the candid eyes, now looked old and ugly. His face was pale and drawn. We were obliged to huddle closer to understand him. He was saying that we had seen a great injustice, but that we must be unwavering in our duty. We must give our lives for the Führer and the fatherland, for the West and for civilization. It was tragic that the Western powers did not as yet see this, but it was bitter indeed that in our own ranks there were those who had no sense of responsibility,enriching themselves from the war, exaggerating everything and making us unpopular. Then he appealed to us to keep our chins up and try to exert a good influence where it was needed, not to forget that the Führer was doing his best and that we must help him. We were all depressed. It took several days before we had our uniforms clean again. Our horror could not be washed away.

From Llgov we wrote home asking to have our civilian things sent to Dreihof. We could scarcely wait to be rid of our uniforms. When the station signs bore German names once more, the weather turned foggy and rainy. We kept the doors of our cars closed. "When I think of home..." we sang, and "It's a long, long way to my home." In the latter song comes the verse about the stooped Jews who walk into the Red Sea; they are engulfed by a wave and the world is well rid of them. We always sang this verse without thinking much about it; in fact, believing it to be funny. If we had stopped to analyze it, we should probably have dismissed it as "coarse soldiers' humor." This time, when we came to that particular verse, Nilus simply said: "Song's ended!" and immediately started singing his favorite: "When the roses last in your garden bloomed."

Dreihof was like the first day: fog, drizzle, gray barracks. There were fresh, ingenuous recruits who looked at us admiringly because we had experienced Russia. We were given our papers; two weeks furlough, after which the Arbeitsdienst would finally be over for us.

On the train home to Cologne we reviewed our situation. Though we had cursed the Arbeitsdienst and our extended involvement in it, we had been spared the front, Stalingrad, the winter in Russia. 1942 was drawing to a close. What would the next year bring each of us? When we caught sight of the cathedral spires of the city, we felt like children again. Mother, our girl friends, our friends, the little motorcycle waiting. We were pleased as punch! As we pulled into the station the air siren sounded and we were immediately herded into the huge air-raid shelter. Bombs exploded, the people became silent, the lights went out, mortar trickled down the wall, and when Jung said: "I think I'd rather have stayed in Malinovska," it did not occur to any of us to laugh.

"Once the war is over, if the *Party* should claim credit for it, you'll perhaps become local commandant in Malinovska. If the *soldiers* should reap the honor, in other words, if the big mouths and one-hundred percenters are thrown out and sensible people run the country, I should like to be sent to America as a diplomat."

"Better shut your trap or before you know it, you'll land in the concert camp or in the jail battalion, where you'll soon be pushing up the daisies."

America, I kept thinking, why the devil did they have to enter the war! We might perhaps bring Russia to her knees, but America-gosh, it's just too far away. If someone had told me that twenty years later I should be making a living and raising a family there, I should probably have begun to believe in ultimate victory.

Chapter Three
1943

It was no use. The infantry had me in its clutches. I tried everything; I even volunteered for the air force. But a sudden case of jaundice put an end to that. On the other hand, the jaundice gave me a few extra weeks at home. This is what happened:

When I came back from the Arbeitsdienst in Russia, I was entitled to a furlough. I spent the time getting acquainted with our new home in Cologne-Lindenthal. Mother had sold our house because we thought the bombs would be more likely to strike us in the more industrialized northern section of Cologne. Moreover, Mother had become a slave to the large house and, without servants, found it impossible to keep it up. True, there were maids recently arrived from Poland, but even they could not be had without a pull. My brother came home on leave from the eastern front and Mother was happy to have us together once more, hale and hearty. When my leave was over, I automatically became a civilian again. That same day I was summoned to the recruiting district headquarters, where a sinister-looking master sergeant ordered me to report for active duty in the artillery. Well, I thought, at any rate better than infantry. He gave me a ticket to Joetaburg for the very next day. "Step into the next room and let the doctor look you over. Just a formality," he snapped.

"Do you have any complaints?" the staff doctor asked me.

Since I visited a doctor only about once every five years, I wondered whether something might ail me. Then it occurred to me that for a few days I'd had a peculiar lump in my throat and that my stool was gray. With an instrument the doctor looked into my eyes and asked whether I had recently been looking yellow. I said no. Whereupon, to my amazement, he said "You have jaundice and will shortly turn bright yellow." I thought I must have misunderstood. But already he took my service-record book and stamped it with the label for which some would have given a fortune: "Temporarily unfit; deferred until January 6th."

The master sergeant couldn't understand it, tore up my traveling orders and quite obviously lost his last shred of faith in the officer corps, specifically the medical branch.

I immediately went up one flight to the air force and volunteered. They seemed delighted and directed me to the clinic where I underwent all kinds of tests. Then I was told: "All O.K. You'll be called up within the next few weeks. May we have your service-record book?" It was only then that the clerk noticed the stamp in my book. That ended my career with the airforce. They required a three-month interval following jaundice.

The army didn't wait that long. On January 8th I became a soldier and an infantryman. The fact that our regiment was called the "grenadier regiment" did not make it any better. Herford was the garrison town and it corresponded to the classical picture: the barracks with the big gate; the high wall over which privates coming in after taps climb with beating hearts; the master sergeant with his company record book sticking out from the second button of his jacket; the wardrobe with the uniforms that were either too big or too small; the canteen grub; the room chores and the short haircut.

After we had been taught to walk, to greet people, to move in public, we were free to go out into the town. Going out in uniform makes a braggart out of a shrinking violet, a beer guzzler out of a temperate man, and skirt-chasers out of married men. It turned me into a successful Casanova. My little garrison honey had all the assets required by a garrison soldier; and I was understandably annoyed when, a few weeks later, we were shipped to Denmark.

I have always found foreign countries fascinating, and it seemed incredible to me that the others could spend days playing cards while the train carried us over bridges, past sea inlets, through charming villages and teeming cities, the names of which were vaguely familiar from geography lessons. What a lovely city Aarhus was! Unfortunately, we were there only a few days and on we went to the island of Fynen, where Nyborg was our final destination. We were billeted in the industrial hotel, a run-down club-style building with ballroom, numerous rooms, garden and courtyard. It was situated in the center of the ancient seaport. Two little sentry boxes at the main entrance were all that betrayed our presence. The second floor had a canteen run by a Dane, and there we could get everything our mess sergeant did not provide: milk, whipped cream, cake, butter and marmalade. For us it was fairlyland. In the shops, meat and poultry were displayed. The hot-dog man cycled through the city drumming up trade. How different from Germany where scant rations had turned fat housewives into mannekin figures.

The air was so fresh, the spring so lovely, we were so young and the war was so far away-no wonder we smiled at the Danish girls and boys! Did they smile back! Russia and Poland were a distant nightmare. Here there was no twaddle about ethnic groups two and three, there were no servants, no inferior human beings. Everything was serene.

First Lieutenant Suck explained the situation in his initial speech. "Denmark is not an occupied country. It is a country we are protecting. We are guests here. We should respect the Danish military here in Nyborg, greet its officers or salute them on duty. Since no one likes to see foreign soldiers in his country, you must avoid singing in the streets. You should exercise caution in maneuvers outside the city; the German authorities are obliged to pay for every tree we scrape. I have nothing against you forming friendships with the Danes, but I must warn you about spies. You are always to go out in twos. Avoid quarrels. Germans are forbidden to dance in public places, by order of the Führer."

First Lieutenant Suck was an elegant guy, so to speak. He could ride well and had social contact with a number of upper-class Danes. There was something aristocratic about him. His Iron Cross, First Class, helped emphasize his masculinity. However, his walk, with both arms drawn back, spoiled that impression. He was popular among his men, but not among the non-commissioned officers. They were a class by themselves and Suck kept them at a distance.

Our first time out was unfortunate. A telephone call summoned our patrol to a bar where a beer-bottle skirmish was going on between German and Danish privates. The reason? The Danes were permitted to dance and our soldiers refused to lend their recent conquests for this purpose. The fist fight was carried out into the street. One of our men was reported for having smashed a bottle on a hard Danish skull.

This incident elicited a brief speech from Suck the next morning. "I've already said that I do not want fights with the Danes. However, I should like to make one thing clear: if a fight cannot be prevented, I want you to strike out in such a way that there will be no troublesome witnesses."

The first sergeants smirked in approval. Janovitz, the fat one, came up to my friend Hannes, gave him a cold grin and said, loud enough for all to hear: "Do you know what that means?"

Hannes did not say anything; evidently he was speechless with fright.

"It means, kill 'em; that's what it means, you jackass."

"Yes sir!"

Suck's magnificent chestnut stallion was already carrying his master out through the gate of the courtyard.

Her name was Benthe, and she was tall, blond and pretty as a picture. I, a mere recruit, had succeeded in taking her away from Lieutenant Held. Thereafter, I was invited to her house for dinner every third evening with one of my comrades. The family was charming. Four daughters, two of them pro-German, the elder engaged to a *landser*. One daughter, of school age, was reserved toward us; the youngest couldn't bear us. Fat mummy always served huge portions. The two-hour repast, with aquavit interludes, was always crowned with an apple *streusel* affair that put everything else into the shade. Then mummy would light a cigar, we would drink another aquavit to peace and good will among the nations and feel supremely content. On weekends we were asked not to put in an appearance, since Father would then be at home; evidently he would not have appreciated our visits. We also formed the habit of looking away when we passed girl friends on the street during the day. In the evening, as soon as the sun set behind the picturesque roofs of the town, every halfway respectable *landser* had his girl on his arm.

One morning, at roll call, First Lieutenant Suck asked: "Can anyone paint or draw?" If a sergeant had asked, I should not have responded, for it would probably have meant the privilege of scrubbing the W.C. with a toothbrush. Hannes and I raised our hands. It was to pay off. First of all, we were asked to draw a horse on a blackboard, so that Suck could point out to his officers' class the various parts of a horse. We were two days drawing our steed and we could not have chosen a better time, for out in the country there were anti-gas defense drills with gas masks.

The second assignment was even better. For the landscape of our quarters a prize was offered to anyone in the division. Hannes and I spent the next fortnight lying on the lawn in front of our building, constructing a mosaic out of little stones and empty cartridge cases. It depicted the Reich eagle with swastika in monumental proportions against a background of white pebbles. Flowers and lawn formed a frame for our artistic effort. Passers-by marveled. Suck grinned, the first sergeants spluttered, whereas our comrades were envious; for while we were going great guns, they were being driven across the training fields.

Hannes and I were gaining an importance and influence. We bartered tobacco-the only scarce article-and succeeded in acquiring a tandem bicycle. No one was more surprised than Suck when we passed him in town on our tandem. It cost him a visible effort to maintain his poise and his correct equestrian bearing.

Once, a soldier died of pneumonia and for some reason he was buried in Fredrickshaven, in the northern part of Denmark. A six-man escort was appointed. Hannes and I among them. We were guests of the Navy for a week. It was princely, and, with slight bitterness, we realized that, though ours was the queen of weapons, we were step children compared to other branches of the service. The burial was brief and dignified, but since we had not known the soldier we were not particularly affected. It meant chiefly one more week's exemption from the routine of disagreeable and strenuous training.

Reports of the bomb terror at home sounded ominous. In March came Mother's telegram announcing the total destruction of our house. Oh God, not that-the irreplaceable furnishings, the antiques and pictures, the thousands of items that were dear to us. To think that it had to hit us! Does anything make sense if our home is reduced to a heap of ashes?

I was given a week's special leave. With borrowed kroner I brought two huge suitcases and two cartons full of food and set out for Cologne. In Hamburg I had a stop-over. I saw the worn and troubled faces, the refugees with the remains of their earthly possessions wrapped in blankets, the bomb ruins, the placards: "Wheels must roll for victory," "Sh-sh-sh the enem is listening," "The Jews are our misfortune," "The Führer is always right." In the waiting room a loud speaker was blaring forth a song by Will Schneider:

> Oh you lord of lies*
> What do I hear you say?
> Wait till Tommy finds you out,
> There'll be hell to pay!

---

*W. Churchill

A Red Cross nurse was leading a blind soldier. A military patrol had a couple of scared-looking youths by the scruff of the neck. Everything was blacked-out, and the table d'hote meal being served in the second class waiting room seemed to consist of shoe leather.

There were two air alarms en route. The train stopped on an open stretch. The lights went out. Spectral search lights streaked across the sky. Anti-aircraft shells crashed and clusters of magnesium lights, like ghostly signposts, directed the fliers to their targets. They were known as "Christmas trees," but "death candles" would have been a more accurate expression. The rumble of hundreds of bombers droned in our ears and clutched at our hearts. The thought of my mother and the loved ones at home numbed me. An old man said, "In Stalingrad our army was defeated, and now we are being buried alive." The remark fell on an awkward silence. A woman said, "The Führer undoubtedly knows what he's doing." The old man started to reply, then seemed to think better of it and lapsed into silence. Well, so what? Things don't look too rosy, but after all we're in it, for better or for worse; we've got to hold out! Did someone say that? I must have thought it.

A conversation was going on next to me.

"What was that about your cousin?"

"Oh, that! Well, it's almost too stupid to talk about. She married a fallen soldier. You've heard of marriage by proxy where the soldier is, say, in Africa..."

"Not any more, my dear man, we're out there too."

"You don't say! Well, then, in Russia, and the bride is in Cologne. So the ceremony is held in two places separately. Well, the latest is this business of marriage with a dead soldier. That's what my cousin did. She was engaged, he was killed, but she was married anyway-to a corpse."

"She must've been expecting a baby."

"Not at all. I'm telling you..."

"Good Lord, is that what they call 'proud mourning'? What'll they think of next?"

And suddenly there was loud guffawing. Not everybody laughed. The woman who had made the remark about the Führer looked irritated and the man in the corner...

The door of the compartment was flung open and an SS patrol demanded our papers. They turned their flashlights on our faces. The man in the corner couldn't find his papers. He looked around desperately and was requested to step outside. He did not return.

The woman said, "All kinds of subhumans are abroad nowadays."

"Now you've said something sensible for a change," the old man snarled, and the woman looked at him in astonishment.

I had to think of Helmut. Two years ago, when I was commuting daily to school, an SS patrol came into the train and demanded our service record books. Helmut's mother is a Jewess. Half-Jews were all released from the armed forces in 1941 and were thereafter slowly but surely looked upon as fair game. His service record book bore the entry in small print: "Mosaic." The SS man leafed through the book, must have seen the word but not understood it; perhaps he thought it was Latin and meant "tubercular." He shrugged and handed the book back to Helmut who was visibly relieved.

Cologne with its spires, my old home town, appeared. No matter what has happened, Mother is well, Hans is alive, almost all my friends are still alive. If only we can live through it! Mother, Hans, grandmother, grandfather, Helmut, Ilse, Mucki-we must live through this damn war!

Then I stood before the ruins of our house. The bridge to my youth nothing but dust and ashes. All the objects that served to bring back memories-a heap of twisted rubbish, black and senseless. Seeing my charred motorcycle was as painful as seeing the grand piano in the front yard, with its three legs pointed upward, like the fingers of a hand raised in solemn oath. Directly beside it lay a wet, half-charred bundle of papers, my school notes and the designs from my engineering school. A neighbor called to me and told me where I could find my mother.

We met again. She was living in the Hotel Monopol where she had reserved a room for me-a royal chamber. I unpacked my bags and there we sat in the cold splender of strange hotel rooms and ate Danish delicacies, recalling old times, trying to make plans for the future. And then we recaptured a family tradition. Whenever things were at their saddest and the moment was least appropriate, we would start to laugh. We laughed ourselves silly; we laughed at ourselves and our misery, at the crazy world, at the few trifles we had managed to save, at the naked Danish pullets. Tears streamed down our faces and, without warning, the thought came to us: we shall survive; we belong to the lucky ones.

Ilse Schaefer came to visit us at the hotel. I knew from mother that, at the risk of her life, she had rescued many of my personal belongings from the burning house. I also knew that she was in love with me and was waiting for me. Alas, I was not in love with her. Trying to avoid a more intimate encounter, prompted simply by a feeling of gratitude and obligation, was awkward and made me rather silent during the rest of my leave.

The remains of our belongings were packed in a moving van, the axle of which finally broke, so that we were on tenterhooks for fear that it, too, might be hit in a new air attack. Mother moved south to Weinheim where she immediately took up the battle with the bomb-damage office.

I traveled back to Denmark with mixed feelings, happy to be reunited with my Benthe in that prosperous country, far from war and air alarms, from destruction and misery.

The attitude of the population seemed to be turning more and more against us and one kept hearing about sabotage. On my birthday, April 9th, the third anniversary of the German march into Denmark, we were not permitted to go out, and I had four hours of patrol duty through the city. About this time we finished our training and everybody began preparing, both physically and mentally, for our transfer to our infantry division and then to Russia.

That evening Suck called me to his quarters. "Heck," he said, "I need a reserve-officer applicant. I should like to recommend you: I know that you have not volunteered. Why?"

"I was eight years old when my father died, and one of the few things I remember him saying was that one ought never to become a soldier, especially not an officer. He must have had his reasons, for he was an officer himself in the First World War. Then there's my brother. For years he's been an infantryman in the thick of it on the eastern front. In every letter he writes: anything but infantry, above all not an officer. Even with the best intentions in the world, I'm just not an officer type. I am a civilian in uniform. I was unable to avoid becoming a soldier and an infantryman. I don't want to become an officer."

Suck had listened to me with a smile; then he laughed aloud. "Heck, you're a crazy guy. You know it, we all know it, and I'll admit I've got a soft spot for you. That's exactly why I'd like to ask you something. Now listen: this is April, 1943. How long do you think the war will last-one year, two years? Scarcely longer. Do you believe your chances of surviving especially as a landser - in Russia - will be greater than if you follow the plan I have in mind for you? Now if you volunteer as reserve-officer applicant you will remain here for the present, until a new course starts in one of the troop training camps. The course will last three months. Then you'll come back to us as an instructor. So next Christmas you'll be spending either with us or on leave. Then you'll have an eight-weeks' probationary period at the front-certainly longer than the average *landser*, but still only eight weeks, whereupon you will attend the officer-aspirants training school. I'm no prophet, Heck, but one thing is probably certain: aside from the eight weeks, you'll be a year and a half in training. It won't be a picnic, but is being a *landser* at the front a picnic? Ask your brother. Think it over. I'll give you two hours' time."

He shook my hand. I was very much impressed by his frankness. I knew he liked me, for I got away with peccadillos for which others would have been punished. Hannes and I discussed the situation; then I accepted Suck's proposal. The small band on my shoulder strap showed that I was a reserve-officer applicant.

A large maneuver was staged to mark the end of our recruiting days. All available units, even the Navy, took part as we simulated an attack on a system of trenches on a rain-swept spit of land, with a wind velocity of ten. The thought that in a few weeks this would be a real experience for most of the men probably made some of them shudder. Nor was I very comfortable when I saw all my comrades going to the Russian front while I remained behind in this never-never land.

Shortly thereafter, a company of reserve-officer applicants came back from the Leningrad front. For me it was reassuring to hear that our division there seemed to be calmly awaiting the end of the war, immobilized in the trenches.

Soon I was bidding my girl friend in Nyborg a painful farewell. But thank God, the plans provided for a brief return to Nyborg as an instructor, after three or four months of training. The course for reserve-officer applicants in Cologne-Wahn was no joke. The training was incredibly difficult and to this day I am ready to beat up Master Sergeant Hirnschal if I ever meet him again. Conditions in such camps have often enough been described. I have nothing to add.

Once, Mother wrote that she was going to Cologne on business connected with our bomb damage. Again she lived at the Hotel Monopol. That night there was a major air alarm and, full of anxiety, I looked out in the direction of Cologne where the Christmas trees were once again lighting up the sky. We heard the thunder of the bombs and the flak shells. Next morning, a tremendous cloud of smoke hung over Cologne. Telephones lines to the Hotel Monopol were dead. Soon the first terrifying reports began coming in. I waited until three o'clock in the afternoon. Then I had a call summoning me to the main guard. And there was Mother. With singed hair and half-burned clothing, she had made her way to Wahn. She had been buried under the wreckage of the hotel for seven hours before she was dug out. Then she had fled over corpses and ruins through the burning city. And here she sat, trembling with exhaustion and fright. I was given a brief leave to take her back to Weinheim. Practically nothing was left of the center of Cologne except the cathedral.

In early autumn I returned to Nyborg, just in time to experience the final hours of a blitz action. We disarmed the Danes and disbanded their army. The reasons given were: espionage, sabotage, underground activity and collaboration with England. In Nyborg there was one dead. Lieutenant Held lost a leg.

The mood of the people changed from unfriendly to scornful. Benthe's sister had her sources of information and knew more about changes in the disposition of our troops than did Suck-who, incidentally, had now become Captain Suck. She told me confidentially, a week in advance, that we would be moved to Ringkoebing, near Esbjerg. There was a big farewell feast at Benthe's home, a final kiss and Nyborg was to become nothing more than a memory.

The halcyon days seemed indeed to have come to an end. Shortly, thereafter, I found myself one of Europe's defenders in a super-bunker off the Atlantic Wall. Amid sand dunes, with a swamp at our backs and the North Sea in front of our noses, we hoped that no one would attack at this point. "Würzburg" was the code name for the radar monster beside our location. It was supposed to tell us how many planes were taking off in our direction from England and at what hour, which was, of course, reassuring to know. Patches of fog, howling winds, driving rain squalls and damp chill in our bare concrete walls did not exactly turn us into satisfied defenders of the West.

Once, Rommel came to visit us. There he stood in my bunker in his long leather coat, wearing a not very distinguished officer's cap which looked like a Party hat. I was disappointed; he looked old and tired. We were momentarily expecting an invasion. Stalingrad, our defeats in Africa, Italy's defection, the intensified bomb terror which evidently could no longer be checked, shifts in high command, the end of effective submarine warfare-it was a year of obvious disintegration of our position. Even stubborn fanatics were now assailed with doubts. Talk about forthcoming miracle weapons came as a spark of hope which seemed to flare up more and more often. Yet slowly but surely, the soldiers became obsessed by one thought: survival is all that matters. In December I was sent home on leave and in January I was to begin my trial stint at the front. Thoroughly trained in the infantry, rested and well fed in Denmark, fortified by a Christmas furlough, I was calmly looking forward to a quiet two-month period on the Leningrad front.

Fate, however, had something different in store for me.

Chapter Four
1944

The train jolted eastward, heads nodding sleepily in time to it. The wooden seats were uncomforable. I had a short wait in Berlin. In spite of war, blackout and air raid alarms, I still felt a trace of Christmas in the air. With four friends, all officer candidates on our way to the front, we were a jolly group. The journey continued through Pomerania, East Prussia and the Baltic states. Snow-covered plains, frozen lakes, frost-encrusted telephone wires leading to lonely farms and sleepy villages-it all looked so peaceful. More and more onion-shaped church spires with Greek orthodox crosses began to appear, and at some stations there were sleighs drawn by strong little horses with bells on their harnesses.

We were on a furlough train and the mood was mixed. There were, first of all, the privates going back to the front after a brief respite. Most of them were disappointed because nothing decisive had happened on the Leningrad front during their absence. This thought was new to me, but would soon become firmly established. A few soldiers from our regiment told us what to expect: a quiet, well-constructed fortification with bulletproof bunkers and communication trenches; a dormant front with practically no nearby firing, but only the distant bombing and rumbling of heavy artillery; a front that had had Leningrad under bombardment for years. After Stalingrad, however, our entire Russian front was shaken. And this was the frightening, disillusioning prelude to a turn of events in the east. Everybody was shocked and all the soldiers embittered by Hitler's funeral oration for the sixth army which, though abandoned, had fought desperately to the end in Stalingrad. Hitler's competence as a commanding general was now universally discussed, criticized and ridiculed. The name of Groefaz,* greatest general of all times, was mentioned. Here in the north we had not suceeded in establishing contact with our armies pushing down from Finland. Leningrad lay in the narrow gap between the two fronts. If we can't take this metropolis, we shall reduce it to ashes, was Hitler's reaction. And so the two fronts were immobilized here. A band of Spanish volunteers, whom the old-timers called the "blue division," had been our neighbors up here for a time. They were good in close combat with knives and slings, but when there were artillery attacks they panicked. They were a plucky, hot-blooded band who finally congealed up here in the north and had to be sent home to thaw out. The entire northern front was expecting new Russian

---

*Abr. of a propaganda expression "groesster Feldherr aller Zeiten"

offensives and my thoughts went back to Captain Suck: "Eight weeks at the front will pass." Let's hope it will remain this quiet, I thought to myself.

We had a day's stop-over in Riga and went sight-seeing. The city was clean, open and laid out on a grand scale, with parks and solidly constructed buildings. I was pleasantly surprised to find a metropolis of this kind in the "uncultivated east." We made the acquaintance of a few German-speaking Estonians and Letts. They were volunteers in the SS and enthusiastic about Nazism. We felt slightly uncomfortable to find these foreigners so devoted to Hitler. Nonetheless, we soon agreed that the peoples of the Baltic were our friends. Thus, I added two new pigeonholes to my file of nationalities. This thinking in categories, in broad generalizations, was typical for us, and still is. For instance, we speak of the laconic, but reliable Norwegians; the smug, "square" Danes; the know-it-all, overly punctilious Dutch; the degenerate, effeminate French; the arrogant, but secretly admired English; the faithful, reliable Finns, Hungarians and Turks; the tough, tenacious, sly Russians; the dishonest, unreliable Czechs; the unclean, primitive, servile Poles; the naive, generous, clever Americans; the profit-seeking, unscrupulous, sharp Jews, the serenading Italians in love with life. Quite apart from their mania for categorizing, the Germans probably needed such patterns of thought in order to find their way about in the jumble of nationalities. The Letts now furnished us with another convenient label by speaking of the drunken, good-for-nothing Lithuanians.

By chance, I visited a large orthodox cathedral in Riga. The service was well attended and I was much impressed by the long-bearded priests in their tall, richly ornamental headgear, by the marvelous rumble of the basses in the imposing choirs, by the grave faces of the churchgoers. We were transferred to cattle cars. It was bitter cold and our little drum stoves glowed. We traveled northeastward through Estonia. On the morning of January 18th, we were told that we had reached our destination. We gathered up our belongings and were about to get off the train when the sirens sounded, planes came swooping down in a lowflying attack, bombs crashed and our train was tossed about. The engine was hit and exploded. In the wild confusion we were scattered, hiding in ditches, under the train, in the station shelter. Scarcely had the dust and smoke cleared and the excitement subsided, when a few heavy artillery projectiles zoomed over our heads and crashed into the houses a few hundred meters beyond. Welcome to the quiet Leningrad front! What the devil's going on here? We had been in the train for days without a radio and without news, and it was only now that we learned at first hand, so to speak, that Ivan had switched over to the offensive.

A young first lieutenant held up a sign bearing the number 126, and since I belonged to the 126th infantry division, I joined the group gathered around him. What he had to say was shattering. The Russians had broken through the position of our division and had partly surrounded it. We were seven kilometers from the front. The name of the town was Gatchina. Our troop could not be reached at the moment. "Hence all those back from leave, all reserve-officer candidates and recruits will be organized into a combat unit," he said. We were to be attached to the 170th division. The worst that can happen to a group of privates is to be attached to another unit as a combat group; nobody knows you, you don't know anybody else, and you are assigned wherever it looks lousy, so that the regulars will be spared.

First of all, we were asked to leave our belongings, all except our bread bags and toilet articles, in one of the houses. That was the last we were to see of them; all my personal belongings and valuables were lost forever. There were 150 of us, and we were marched off immediately, past the large castle which had been the winter residence of the Czar's family. A corporal told me that he had once visited this castle and that the Czarina's bedroom was filled with erotica of all kinds, and that the structure was exhibited which Catherine had used when she copulated with a donkey. The thought was not exactly cheering. After a long march, chilled to the bone, we reached the collective farm, Teizi. It was already dark, although it was early in the day. Here, each of us was given a brand-new white outer uniform with felt boots, an old carbine, thirty-six rounds of ammunition and three hand grenades. Then we were divided into groups. I was made the leader of the third group. Two of my friends were in it; all the others were strangers. I wrote down everybody's name and home address. In the distance we heard the barking and rumbling, the whistling and crashing of the front. The sky flickered red and white. After we had had a few slices of bread and butter with sausage and cheese, we were given a ration of whiskey. With mixed emotions, we lay down for the night on the wooden floor of the empty room and covered ourselves with our overcoats.

We were shaken out of a sound sleep by an incredible crash. Window panes flew out and hundreds of roof tiles clattered down into the courtyard. It was still dark and the clock said four. We ran downstairs and were met by laughing *landsers* who explained that this was the retort of a long-range gun that had been put in position outside the house. Two more shots followed, whereupon the artillerymen started to take the thing down again. The monster looked like a circus cannon that spews out living acrobats.

An hour later we were on our way. We were ordered to attack Krasnoje Selo. When the day dawned we were lying in position, widely distributed over a hollow between thin bushes. As the morning fog lifted like a stage curtain, we saw, to our horror, that the hill in front of us was alive with Russians. We now heard the rattle of tanks puncuated by the cursing of soldiers striking their little horses. The idea of storming this hill with thirty rounds of ammunition and 150 men was absurd and was apparently given up, for the lieutenant now had us retreat cautiously and reassemble. Once again we were tramping through the snow. It was a miracle that the Russians had not caught sight of us. After some time we reached a village. The winter uniforms, all in white, and the felt boots kept us beautifully warm. It was rumored that there had been a falling-out between our lieutenant and a colonel. We were grateful to the former, who was decorated with a top medal for bravery, for releasing us from our impossible position.

Daylight was all too brief. Again it grew dark, and dense fog covered the little village like a shroud. We were asked to speak in whispers. Rattling metal parts were muffled with foot wrappers. Again the groups were separated. Then came the order: "We shall defend this town. The position must be held under all circumstances. For the defense there is a battalion here from the division 'Grossdeutschland,' a unit that is armed to the teeth. We shall relieve these men. The group leaders will immediately inspect their sections. Take-over in exactly one hour."

My heart was in my throat as I crept behind the lieutenant into the defensive trench. One could hardly see three meters ahead. From the distance, in all directions, front, sides and rear, flash signals rose up. We heard the thunder of cannonading and sometimes the terrible hiss of our rockets that carried their lethal burdens like meteors through the foggy night. Here in the trench it was quiet. We nodded our heads in greeting to the grateful privates whom we were relieving. They were already pushing toward the exits. The trench was almost up to our hips; there was no bunker, no dugout, no hold. The section for my group was about 150 meters long. I had a brief whispered conversation with the departing group leader. He said that during the day the Russians were at a distance of approximately 500 meters in a wooded section. He inquired about our arms and shook his head in disbelief. "Without machine guns you're finished before you start," he said dryly. I looked at the new assault guns of his men like a pupil admiring a Mercedes racing car. I asked whether he had had heavy losses, but did not wait for an answer. I felt slightly unwell and crawled between the legs of a stiffly frozen Russian corpse lying halfway across the trench. Then I fetched my men, put them all, for the time being, on double sentry in the trench, within calling distance, and permitted each post an hour's sleep in the trench. I crept as far as my neighbors in either direction, back to the village, then once more up and down the entire trench. Now I was familiar with every foot of it and felt better. The night was endless and damp. It was thawing somewhat and puddles were forming at the bottom of the trench.

Early in the morning we were given combat chocolate and one-fourth bottle of schnapps* each. We were relieved when the fog cleared and the

*Hard liquor.

sun rose. We looked about inquisitively. In front of the trench, and even behind it, lay numerous bodies, partly covered with drifting snow. In front of us was a broad plain which finally terminated in a wooded hill. So that's where the enemy is, I said to myself.

We were now joined by an observer in advanced position from the heavy infantry guns. We also finally received a machine gun with six cases of ammunition. Then at nine o'clock, when cold pea soup was served courage and good spirits returned. Our position was well laid out and must have been difficult to detect, especially with our white uniforms. Though our armament was primitive, it sufficed for an infantry attack. After that, we would have to see. Having the "heavy gun" man around was also somewhat reassuring.

At exactly eleven o'clock in the morning the unexpected happened. I was looking along the edge of the wood with my binoculars when suddenly, without a shot having been fired, thousands of Russians emerged like ants and swarmed toward us. Not a sound, not a shot. I could not believe my eyes. I called all my men to their posts and we looked at each other dumbfounded. There was nothing for it-there they were coming toward us. In long dark coats, in brilliant sunshine, on a white field of snow. Hundreds, thousands, Why, it's simply idiotic! With fingers on our triggers we sat rigid in our trench and waited. The observer whispered into his instrument and when the Russians were as close as the length of a football field our heavy guns charged. They shot ricochets, that is, projectiles which hit the snow in front of the enemy, rebound and explode directly above the enemy. The effect was simply horrible. Many rushed desperately forward. They became victims of our machine gun fire. Others ran back. Most of them were torn to shreds, or let themselves drop, in order to bury themselves in the snow. In fifteen minutes it was all over. Not a single Russian had come within calling distance of us and the last mushroom of smoke hung in the air like a question mark. Why? What sort of senseless massacre was this? Even now, I'd be interested to know what had motivated the Russians. We spent the rest of the day sharpshooting at anything that was still moving over there, since we did not wish a nocturnal surprise.

In the village a dressing station was set up. A chaplain came through the trench in the afternoon. He spoke a few words to each one. We forgot to make fun of him; after all, he had pushed his way this far. He made the sign of the cross toward the dead Russians and said, "They too are God's children."

When it grew dark again, we knew that this night would bring combat. We crouched into corners, smoked cigarettes at the bottom of the trench, and hoped that everything would soon be over. A rather desperate wish, since it looked rather as though everything were about to begin.

For me the end came toward midnight. The entire front seemed in a turmoil. There was thunder from all sides and magnesium lights flared up. For seconds thereafter an ashen light hung over the graveyard in front of us and we stared across hoping-yes, sometimes hoping that the miracle weapons, about which there had been more and more talk lately, would finally shorten the war.

A barrage of shots alerted us, then came the whistling and humming of flying shells. Here and now we young officer aspirants had our baptism of fire. Ear-splitting crashes, the earth bursting asunder, hits right and left, then a lull.

There had been no direct hit, no one was wounded, everybody had been lying deep in the trench. We knew, of course, that an attack was imminent. All posts were occupied. Our machine gun lay covered up in a niche. Fresh ammunition was being passed out when there was a new burst of fire. I was just handing an empty cartridge case back over my shoulder when a shell struck the edge of the trench in front of me. I felt as though something had struck my arm off. The explosion knocked me down. With a horrible taste of sulphur in my mouth and a droning in my head I got up and felt the upper part of my arm. A big hole in my uniform, blood streamed out of my arm down to my hand. My arm hung lifeless. Cautiously I tried to move my fingers and was relieved to note a slight reaction. I felt no pain. I was about to call over to my neighbor that I was wounded when the shelling ceased, only to be followed immediately by a wild yelling and shooting. "*Hurrae!*" the Russians shouted as they came dashing toward our trench. "They're coming!" one of our men yelled: "Fire, fire, kill them, the bastards!" I held my heavy rifle in my left hand, but shooting was impossible. In front of me and behind me a couple of dark figures leaped into the trench and a wild tussle began. I yelled to Angermann that I was wounded and would have to have help. He waved, laughed and, brandishing a spade, rushed at an approaching Russian. That was the last I was to see of my group.

The loss of blood made my knees buckle. I ran back to the communication trench, threw my rifle into a dugout, clutched my wound and dashed into the farmhouse with its dressing station. There the medical orderly was bandaging a *landser* by the light of a candle. He cut off all the sleeves on my right arm with scissors and looked at the wound. A helluva hole, black from powder and burn, red from blood pulsating out of the wound. He applied muslin bandages and put my arm in a sling. He had just finished when the door flew open and the candle blew out. In the door frame, tall and broad, with a high fur cap, stood a Russian. His silhouette against the leaping flames of the burning huts looked gigantic. With a mighty leap I reached the back door, fell into the wet snow, picked myself up and dashed off. Behind me, the windows of the house blew out in an explosion. I heard cries of "Hurrae" and "Hurrah," and the sound of hand grenades and rifle shots. When I reached the edge of the wood, the sky glowed red. Behind me there was hand-to-hand fighting in the burning village. In the distance, smoke-shell mortars were coursing through the night. Here, on the wood path, it grew quieter the farther I went. I knew that Teizi lay in this direction. It was disturbing to see light rockets going up to the right and left, even in front of me. I had but one thought: to get out of this mess.

The collective farm was closer than I had realized. There, a main field-dressing station had hastily been set up. Hundreds of wounded soldiers were lying about. However, my turn soon came. The doctor removed my bandages, cauterized the edge of the wound, applied new bandages and asked about the situation at the front. He looked anxiously at all the wounded. "Our only Red Cross car is outside and about to drive off. Try to get on it," he said. I swung myself onto the running board of the moving car. A bumpy ride of ten kilometers and we were back in Gatchina which I had left only three days before.

The town was in wild disorder. Civilians and soldiers were packing boxes and bundles; an attempt was being made to stow away a front library in a horse-drawn vehicle. Isolated artillery hits exploded in the midst of all this. On the market square we were picked up by a bus loaded with the lesser wounded, and soon we were jogging along on bumpy, icy roads forty-five kilometers to Siviskoye, a miserable hamlet crammed with refugees and soldiers.

One thing Siviskoye had that was worth its weight in gold: a waiting hospital train. The rations and the care we had on this train which belonged to the SS were marvelous. Soon we were steaming off to the west. I have a wound entitling me to home leave; how wonderful! My arm will heal and be as good as new! I thought of everybody at home and how astonished they'd be to see me returning, a wounded warrior.

It was early morning when I awoke. The train was standing still and outside in the dark I heard women's voices speaking German. They were Red Cross nurses. Fifty lightly wounded men were taken off here and transferred to an ambulance. Minutes later we drove into the yard of what looked like a new hospital. There were foreign words printed on the door; so we had not made it to Germany! My dream of home leave was over. We were in Kedeinas in Lithuania, not too far from the East Prussian border. Again I was in luck. The head doctor was Dr. Adams, the former student leader of my district. He had my arm mended within seven weeks-much too soon for me, but not for my arm, the further use of which I had about written off as lost. He gave me a number of minor posts, but even he could not manage a home leave for me. Incidentally, he was somewhat of an individualist. The doctors in his division were all first lieutenants, whereas he had remained a medical noncommissioned officer. He always seemed to foul things up when it came time for promotions. Not professionally. As a physician he was fantastic. I remember one of his patients was an SS man with a leg wound which necessitated shortening one leg. Though a commission had advised amputation, Adams had shortened the man's other leg as well, so that he would not become a cripple. The trouble with Adams was alcohol, but in that respect he was not unique.

Kedeinas was a small hamlet. The Lithuanians were scarcely distinguishable from the Poles. The muffled figures one saw from the hospital windows all seemed to be blowing liquid clouds in front of them. On Sundays, German school children would come to visit us. They sang for us and their pure voices and good will moved us very much. When we found out about them and where they came from, we became acquainted with a new hopeless chapter in the history of the Third Reich, which will probably never become generally known.

One Sunday we were invited by a few of these German peasants to spend the day on their farms. It was a cold, clear, dry and sunny day when the farmer bundled me into his large sleigh. Two sturdy horses were blowing steam from their nostrils and bells were tinkling on the harnesses as we drove off. The farmer was wearing a huge Persian lamb cap, the fur of which, along with his eyelashes, eyebrows, mustache and woolen shawl, were covered with hoarfrost. One's skin felt taut and it was almost too cold to breathe. Soon we had our shawls wrapped around our faces and when our noses got too white, they had to be rubbed. The horses trotted along on the endless plain and the snow-covered road showed but a single track. After about forty-five minutes we reached a short, treelined road that led straight to the farm. Here the whole family was gathered in their Sunday best to greet me. After I was introduced, amid cordial assurances of pleasure and honor, I was led into the house. The preparations were for a guest honor, and I kept having the feeling that I did not deserve this. After we had dined, I learned their story.

They were Swabians and came from Bessarabia. For generations under the Russian czars they had been well off and retained their own language and customs. After the First World War their homeland became Rumanian, so that they escaped Bolshevism. In 1940 the Soviet Union demanded the return of Bessarabia, wereupon 85,000 German peasants who did not choose to live under the Soviets started their long trek back into the Reich. It had always been their wish, they told me, to return to the land of their forefathers. Full of pride, they had heard of Germany's rise under Hitler, and the watchward "Home to the Reich" had passed from one to the other like a torch. Thus they left their homes and their beautiful, prosperous farms and traveled to Poland in long, covered-wagon caravans. Yes, to Poland. Germany policy in the east had big plans for them but the time was not yet ripe and so they were kept in camps. Then, when the war was carried into Russia, they were settled in this region of Lithuania. Or what you might call settled. The Polish peasant was driven from his farm; he was slowly going under in this miserable Lithuanian village. The German peasant was declared master and the farm was handed over to him. Thus he became a militiaman who carried a rifle into his field. For over a year now the dogs of the dispossessed Poles howled at night around their former homes. The Germans had set to work and made a model farm of the dilapidated property. They were even trying to make friends with the Poles, but the east-territory policy which was being carried on senselessly and incompetently here as everywhere by German Party members was stronger. Thus, in a strange country, surrounded by hate and vindictiveness, they had resigned themselves to building up and defending a life which they had never really wanted. No wonder all their hopes were centered on our retreating front. Heavens above, if the German army fails us, where shall we go? We shall be homeless, and in our dream home, Germany, we shall be burdensome foreigners for whom there is no place. I was getting too warm and not feeling very well. If only I had something cheerful to report! After a few good drinks and some rousing songs, they told stories about their former home, and tears rolled down their weathered faces.

A few days later I made the acquaintance of two pretty blond girls from Dresden who were teaching the farm children. They lived in the village and felt quite isolated. They told me that the school and the children on their way to school were monitored by an SS staff. They themselves had come east out of idealism and they both believed in our ultimate victory as others believe in the Bible. They gave me their address and told me to visit them when my arm was better. I suspected adventure, and two weeks later I set out with a friend. It was almost dark when we stumbled through the dull village. Here and there a drunk lay in the gutter, and my companion murmured something about ether imbibed undiluted by these fellows, whereupon they are knocked out completely for a while. Who knows whether it was true. In any case, we had made the mistake of not announcing our visit, and what we discovered was certainly unexpected. Three SS guys were reeling about in the apartment, the door of which stood ajar. My two idealists were giving a naked demonstration, rolling about on the floor. Fortunately, they recognized us, which calmed the SS men somewhat. We quickly fled, and two days later the girls visited us at the hospital to apologize. They wept inconsolably and blamed everything on loneliness and alcohol; finally the head nurse arrived and threw them out.

Entertainment groups on assignment in front hospitals helped to pass the time. I was still hoping for a furlough, but on March 30th I was finally declared fit and was packed on a train for Wilna, the assignment center for personnel in transit. I was on my way back to my division to begin my probationary period anew. Eight weeks. Those three days before did not even count. However, I had achieved one thing: the wound stripe (purple heart).

In the railroad shack at Wilna, I sat over a small beer and thought things over. Two years before, just drafted, I had been proud to be able to serve my country, not that I would have volunteered for anything. No, it was simply a matter of being one of those who, in times of crisis, does his bit along with all the others who are carrying out a large, unifying idea. If one has to be a soldier, one might as well be a good one and bring good will and idealism to the task. That had been my way of thinking two years ago. Today the world looked very different. Now, I told myself, what counts is to steer clear of the hot spots, gain time, be sent on leave, mistrust everything political, keep one's fingers off anything dangerous, critically weigh everythig that is said officially, be skeptical of all big talk, all idealists-that was how I felt as I sat there on the freshly wiped table in the dim station barracks of Wilna.

I looked up to see in front of me an obviously very drunk soldier. He dropped onto a bench at my table. Then he bawled for a waiter. After a long draught, he sized me up. "Well, sergeant, where you going, front or home? Front's a lot of shit, but my job's not exactly a joyride either." Then he laughed a drunken laugh. It did not take me long to identify his uniform: SS man with the rank of corporal, Iron Cross 2d class, on the lower part of the sleeve a stripe with something disagreeable on it, I've forgotton what, operational command or Skull and Crossbone special unit or something on that order. He dug into his watchpocket and pulled out a large diamond ring. "Oh well," he observed, "sometimes one has a few breaks."

I had the feeling that something disagreeable was about to happen. "What do you mean?" I had not meant to ask it. But now he moved next to me and said, "My job is in Warsaw. We guard the ghetto, see, the Jews, stupid pigs. Big mess, miserable lot I'm telling you."

I did not say anything, staring into my empty glass and experiencing a mounting feeling of shame. I did not look at him. He smelled of beer and cigarette smoke which he seemed to swallow. Now he took a swig from a bottle he was carrying and belched loudly.

"Those Jews are stupid cowards," he continued. "They'll give anything for their lopsided lives. Now I'll tell you how we work it. Every morning I round up 100 Jews and take them to work on a railroad section. We count'em, see? Well, in the evening I bring 'em back into the ghetto-a hundred of 'em. Of course, they're limp as rags and sometimes one of 'em'll keel over at work. So when I fetch 'em back to the ghetto, there'll be ninety-nine and a stiff. The corpse isn't necessarily a Jew, you see, no you don't see." He lowered his voice and kept looking around. "Let's say there's a rich Jew who wants to get away. So I make a deal with him in the ghetto. For three diamond rings I let him go. Before he disappears, he gives me his coat with the star of Israel on it. Then I pick out a stupid Polack, conk him over the head and take him back to camp as a dead Jew. Big deal, eh? That way, everybody's satisfied, and that Jew won't get very far anyhow; why, they don't even know enough to cut off their long locks."

My train was announced. Two minutes later I was sitting in the empty compartment on a hard wooden bench and the train started puffing off in the direction of the front. The lights of the Wilna station streaked by and in the frosted windowpane I looked into my own eyes and thought: just a few months ago I would have reported this chap. Today I realized too much was wrong. I had to think of Helmut. Mother wrote that they were now obliged to remain in hiding. Why could these few harmless individuals not be left in peace? But here in the east things seemed to be far worse. Once this damn war is over, I thought, we'll clean house with these scoundrels. But who will be running things after the war, the Party or we, the returning soldiers? With my thoughts in turmoil, I tried to get some sleep.

All during that trip eastward my thoughts wandered. It looked bad for our armies in the east and the south. Our allies and friends, the Finns, Bulgarians, Rumanians, Hungarians, even the Italians had deserted us or were on the point of giving up. Once more we were alone. In Italy the Americans were marching on Rome. Mussolini, overthrown, rescued by the whizz Skorszeny, had now become the butt of ridicule. The founder of Fascism, the hero of a new Imperium Romanum, had been reduced to nothing and his days were numbered. It was hard for us to swallow, and we had the tendency to regard the serenading Italians as southern ne'er-do-wells. In point of fact, we Germans had not expected anything different from the Italians; they were simply not born for greatness. Here in Russia, the Stalingrad turning-point had shaken our confidence in the supreme command. Anyone who still believed in victory would have to count on the miracle weapon about which there was so much talk. Anyone who was not prepared to stake everything on victory had the choice of "unconditional surrender," a concept that had meanwhile insinuated itself into our consciousness, or he would be forced to try to revolt against our leaders. The latter idea was absurd and certainly not feasible for the average citizen. Then there was the oath which, as soldiers, we had sworn to our supreme commander, Hitler. Thus, propaganda was directed against "moral swinishness" and appealed to us not to perjure ourselves and forsake the fatherland in its hour of need.

It was impossible for our leaders to give up the war as hopeless. We had been informed of America's Morgenthau policy, and Goebbels shouted it into his propaganda: They want to turn us into a defenseless, hopeless agrarian state stripped of any rights! This idea made a mockery of the Treaty of Versailles, the treaty which had become the nutritive soil for a Hitler and the ultimate reason for the present war.

The Atlantic Wall stretched from Narvik to Biarritz, and a large-scale invasion was expected. Yet in spite of all the proganda that spoke of invincible fortifications, the *landsers* who had been there had their own ideas about its invincibility. The positions were inadequately defended by men who were either too young or too old. Our armies in France? Every *landser* said they had been sitting around too long; they were soft, inexperienced in combat and listless. Why aren't they systematically interchanged with the armies in the east? Here in Russia the command seemed to be counting on the old divisions that had been tussling with Ivan for years. SS task forces were put in at crucial points and they were doing the best they could. Even Goering, whose air force was accomplishing less and less, was permitted to mobilize a division. This, too, superbly armed and manned with young people, was doing its utmost. The endlessly long front had been shortened. Incredibly difficult battles had made sullen enemies of the two opponents, who knew no mercy and honored no Geneva Convention.

The bombing of our defenseless homeland and the civilian losses had undermined morale, whereas, on the other hand, they showed those who were ready to capitulate exactly what they could expect from the other side. One soldier with whom I spoke on the train said, "When you're face to face with a Russian, the problem is no longer 'Better dead than a slave' but rather 'Better fight honorably for Germany than croak in Siberia or be bombed in Germany or, after a lost war, reap the harvest sown by a few criminals.' Versailles was a foretaste-miserable starvation will then be the order of the day."

If only all this would end soon, I was foolish enough to think-but, damn it all, how could it end? And then the vision of our injustices arose. The face of the SS man in Wilna seemed to sneer at me from the black pane of the compartment window.

Then I thought of Mother and my brother Hans and hoped (I had never learned to pray properly) that they would survive this war. As for me, I was quite sure that I would. With what was left of our possessions, Mother had now found refuge in Weinheim near Heidelberg. Hans continued to remain in the center sector of the eastern front. As "Corporal East" with the "frozen meat decoration"* and important medals, he bore the taint of immortality, though the record would express it differently. I also dreamed about Mucki, my Platonic friend, who wrote to me faithfully. My dreams did not remain Platonic, and I was thoroughly annoyed when the shrill whistle woke me up. We had arrived. Eight weeks, I muttered, eight weeks - and crossed my fingers.

My regiment was in a fortified position at the southern end of Lake Peipus. We were on the edge of a swampy terrain. Because of this there was no question of digging in; the location had been built upward and was known as a palisade. This defense installation had been built months before by the Todt organization, a civilian work unit with foreign helpers. As one approached it from the rear, it presented the following picture: A

---

*A decoration for having spent the winter 1941-42 in Russia.

thin stand of pine was interpersed with areas of heath and swamp. Sandy roads led to the battalion bunkers which were squat log houses with grass growing on their many-tiered, beamed roofs. From there, narrow paths, some of them corduroy dams, led to the bunkers making up the living quarters of the front line in the troop bunkers one could only crawl; they were a tight squeeze, dark, and meant only for sleeping. Corduroy dams over quicksand led from here up to and along the palisade. The latter was merely a wooden wall approximately eight feet high and three and a half feet deep. Sand had been pressed between the outer and inner walls and here and there apertures had been left that served as lookouts and loopholes. In our sector of the company, the wall skirted the swamp. Our mine zone was spread out in front of the wall and consisted of barbed wire entanglement and warning indicators. No man's land was an open section of sandy soil with small bushes and hollows that sloped very slightly upward toward the enemy position. Behind and hence in the lee of our palisade, we were free to walk about unseen by the enemy. Infantry missles did not penetrate the wall. The position was quiet. After heavy fighting in Leningrad, my regiment had moved into this prepared position; the Russians were apparently reassembling and bringing in reinforcements. From Rostov we could hear the thunder of cannonading. The weather was pleasant and still too cool for gnats. We were full of lice, as we were everywhere in Russia. I was immediately put in charge of a group and a sector. I did not know any of my new comrades.

I became acclimated very soon. This time, it seemed, I had drawn a quiet sector. For a week absolutely nothing happened. Then we had two dead at the hands of Russian sharpshooters who, well camouflaged, were lying in wait somewhere in the foreground. They had aimed at a loophole in the wall and, on each occasion, inflicted fatal head wounds. Once, a *landser* reported to me that a major with a wolf hound had inspected the sector at night. The warning came hours too late. It had been a camouflaged Russian, a so-called front-runner who, by this time of course, was far away. We also had such front-runners, and twice we were advised to focus our attention on a certain sector at a certain hour. Sure enough, the man appeared at the right, crossed over and was immediately relayed to the division.

In the evening, under a bright moon, in the shelter of our palisade, we sat on the corduroy dam, smoking, drinking a little and unconcernedly singing our familiar songs. The front was then hushed and, if we paused, the Russians would start singing. At this point, they were about 300 feet away in a network of trenches that was growing ever deeper. During the day we observed them through our scissors telescope and noted every movement. At night we would send small listening detachments into the area on the immediate front. Once, a special defense detachment arrived. I had to take one of these men out. We crept as far as the Russian wire where he jabbed a wire rod into the ground and left it. From now on our defense was able to listen to all telephone conservations over there.

Easter and my birthday fell on the 9th of April. The surprise came at midnight. We were suddenly pulled out of our positions. Our neighbors took over our sector along with their own. Then it was announced that thirty kilometers south of the Russians we had succeeded in making a breakthrough and that we were needed there for a short time as reinforcements. We piled into trucks that jolted us through the starry Russian night. It was still dark when we were unloaded on a farm and were immediately marched off in groups. My neighbor nudged me and pointed to a pile of corpses, at least fifty of them, stacked against the house wall. I could not tell whether they were Russians or Germans. I felt slightly ill at the sight. From up ahead the message was relayed that everyone was to remain extremely quiet. We crept onto a brown field, then up a hill. Now we saw the suggestion of a trench. Two men were posted every thirty meters and ordered to dig in as quickly as possible. Heavens! I thought, this was an unprotected forward-slope position. We dug in like moles. When day dawned we were all in deep holes. Then the sun rose and if one of us so much as moved, we were shot at from somewhere. We spent the entire Easter Sunday, my twenty-first birthday, in our holes without moving, without eating, without contact or communication. Was it any wonder that we longed for the night! It came and brought a swarm of men. Scarcely had twilight set in when Russian *hiwis*,* former prisoners willing to work for us, appeared. They were friendly Mongolians under German supervision who, with hoe and spade, set to work to dig the connecting trenches. Toward midnight a penal battalion was sent in. Unarmed, with guards, they represented all branches of the service, with neither insignia of rank nor decorations. It was a dangerous mission. They were obliged to lay out rolls of barbed wire at a considerable distance in front of our trench. They, of course, could not remain hidden from the enemy and light flares were immediately sent up. For seconds the men would freeze on the spot and take on the appearance of tree stumps in front of our trench. Then would come the rat-tat-tat of a machine gun, a cry somewhere-and feverishly the work would continue.

Two o'clock in the morning found us in a chest-deep trench with substantial shelters and battle positions. We had scarcely had time to worry about Russians who apparently were occupied with their own defenses.

After some five hundred feet our hill terminated in a hollow covered with brush, which gradually led into woods. That was where the enemy was dug in. We heard them all day long when we were not sleeping. Our

---

*Abr. for Hilfswillige (Those willing to help).

position was lightly guarded during the day, while most of us slept. At night everybody worked on the position. Next, we built a troop shelter with plank beds. After a week without combat, we felt we were ready, come what may. Ivan was rattling his tanks behind the woods and we knew that an attack was imminent. However, we had been there three weeks now and nothing had happened-or practically nothing. There are only two things to report about this interval. First, the frogs. It had rained during the night and at dawn, as I crawled through the trench, I found masses of frogs in the bottom of the trench. They had hopped in from the field and were unable to get out. There was a professional chef in my group, and he realized that this might mean the climax of his service. That night we had frogs' legs in butter, as many as we could hold. They were delicious. We sent a panful to the commanding officer who thereupon came forward himself to admire our frog paradise and order our cook to headquarters.

Then there was the business with scraping noises. One night, the guard wakened us and told us to listen. Sure enough, those were undoubtedly spades we heard below us. In order to rule out any error, I ordered absolute quiet throughout the entire section. We put our ears to the ground. No doubt about it, somebody was digging below us. We reported this to the higher-ups, but nothing happened. Three days later we were evacuated from the position and taken back to the palisade. We sighed with relief. Everybody realized that we were very fortunate to have circumvented any number of eventualities. We had two days off duty at the regimental command post, during which we were deloused, took showers, put our uniforms in shape and wrote letters. For a change, we also had mail from home. Then, rested and refreshed, we returned to our palisade home in the swamp.

Meanwhile the Russians had not been idle. Their trench network had been expanded and in front of it they had placed mines and barbed wire. At one point they had thrust out an intersecting trench and placed a machine-gun bunker directly in front of us. What really burned us up was the fact that this was a captured German gun, an MG-42, the swiftest and best of the war. During the day, the Russians left the advanced position unoccupied, but at night they shot their sheaves of fire along our entire front. Hence it was not surprising that our commander ordered a change. He spoke somewhat as follows:

"Comrades," he said, "at the moment we've come to a dead end in the war. Our lives are safer here than at home. Let us not forget, however, that this is a fateful period in the history of our people. We cannot afford to lie back and do nothing. I have therefore decided to smoke out the Russian nest in front of our position by means of an assault detachment, and at the same time to take prisoners. We need prisoners to find out what the enemy has in mind. We have a week to get everything ready; we will have the assistance of the artillery, the combat engineers and the aerial reconnaissance. We shall try to use only volunteers. The leader of the assault troop will be ROB* Sergt. Kampmann, his substitute and leader of the second group will be ROB Sergt. Heck, the leader of the third group, Corporal Schmidt."

So that was it. Proving my fitness at the front. Eight weeks without shooting would have been too good to be true. So now it would be an assault troop.

With the help of excellent aerial photographs, a model of the entire section was made in the sand box. Hundreds of details were discussed. Then, at the last minute, the operation was postponed for two days.

On that first night, one of our tracer bullets had set fire to the foreground and, to our delight, some 300 Russian mines went off, one after the other. The entire front was alerted and illumined by the bush fire and the explosions. Thus, the already present mine deactivators from the combat-engineer battalion were superfluous. That same evening they gave us a lesson on the subject of Russian mines.

The next night was also beyond our control. A propaganda company suddenly appeared, set up loud speakers on the palisade, played a few Russian folksongs for the benefit of the enemy and then delivered long, impassioned speeches to the Russians, urging them to throw away their weapons and defect to our side. We were ordered to look for defectors and not to shoot throughout the night. Not a living soul appeared and our commander grew pale with fury at the all-powerful propaganda machine. Thus, the assault took place on the third night.

It was midnight. The air was cool and clear. A layer of clouds covered the stars and the darkness was a welcome ally. From the moment we departed through a hole in the palisade, we were obliged to crawl. Kampmann with his four men was in the lead, then came Schmidt's group, while I was last with my four men. In a long row we wriggled our way though the gap familiar to us in the tangle of wire and mine on our front. We had been given eight minutes, and that is exactly what it took before the last man reached the scarcely perceptible sandy depression in the foreground. Kampmann and his group remained there, while Schmidt moved eighty meters to the right parallel to the front and my group the same distance to the left. Ten minutes had been provided for this maneuver. Now I was alone with my men; to our rear, the safety of the palisade, our world; in front of us, the enemy; around us a no man's land that we had studied until we knew it by heart. I had been this far twice on listening-post duty. I looked at my watch. It was time to start crawling toward the Russian trench. In a row, one behind the other, we now had to crawl forward on our bellies. All three groups had twenty minutes to reach the Russian trench.

---

*Reserve-officer applicant, noncomissioned officer.

Carrying my pistol in my right hand and probing the earth with my left, I struggled forward. Whatever you do, don't make a sound. The farther we can get without being detected, the better. My hand bumped against a box mine, the size of a cigar box. For a moment I hesitated. Damn it all, I thought, they covered the place with mines again last night while we were waiting for deserters. Gently I lifted the cover, carefully took out the fuse, threw it two meters to the left and handed the deactivated mine to Wallerstein behind me, whose mud-streaked face registered a smile that became a grimace. I handed him six more mines before we reached the barb wire. I extricated the wire shears from my belt, rolled over on my back, waited until a shot fell somewhere and snipped one wire after another. Eighteen in all. There seemed to be no end to them. I pushed the spirals aside, thus making a passage about two meters wide.

It was quiet; not a sound came from our friends at the right. Have they managed to get through, I wondered? Schmidt had not been present at the mine lesson. Wonder if he...? I crawled on. Now the machine-gun bunker was clearly visible, then the edge of the trench. Another thirty meters. Softly, whatever you do, don't make a sound. Now we heard the Russians coughing, talking, spitting in their dugouts. I was heading toward the trench embankment ten meters to the left of the bunker. Once I looked over my shoulder; my men were close behind me. I kept staring at the black loopholes in the bunker and trusting my lucky star. Suddenly a clatter in the bunker. For seconds we froze in horror as the Russians sent a few bursts of fire into the night, a hair's breadth from our heads. Had they seen us? No, they must have directed a few routine shots at the palisade, just to show us that they were still around. We crawled another ten meters, another five. Now the wind carried the smell of the Russian Mahorca tobacco to our nostrils. I reached the two-foot trench embankment and squeezed against it lengthwise. The others followed. I looked at my watch: exactly as we had planned. My heart was pounding like mad. Wonder if the others had made it?

We heard footsteps in the trench, a door banged, two men were laughing.

With extreme caution I pushed aside a little sand from the edge of the trench and looked directly at the back of the Russian's head. On the other side of the trench, behind the Russian, a door opened and blocked my view for a few seconds. The Russian walked to the door and shut it from the outside. Then he disappeared to the right into the bunker. The door must have led to a dugout that we had not yet discovered, perhaps a sleeping bunk or ammunition chamber. Directly opposite was the bunker covered with beams and earth. Three men were in there now, perhaps a couple more in the dugout. I now took two minutes to catch my breath, and as I looked toward my men who were waiting soundlessly, pressed against the trench embankment, I reviewed the situation in my mind.

The first phase had clicked, as in a manuever. Plan One had

stipulated that we were to push forward undetected to the Russian trench. Ten other possibilites of what to do if this or that should happen had been provided for. But everything had worked out well. Here we lay at the edge of the Russian trench and the others had probably also come this far. I was now faced with the second phase. The time had come; we had to go on.

Suddenly, from the right a brief suppressed cry and a pistol shot. I waited for the agreed-upon cry of "Hurrah," but nothing happened. So I, too, decided to plunge over the trench wall into the interior. Within seconds we had all disappeared into the trench. Three of my men immediately ran to the left, to the next bend in the trench where their task was to block it off. I gave Wallerstein my automatic pistol; he handed me a load of dynamite. I immediately pulled the fuse cord and counted. Those were the longest seconds of my twenty-one years. We were still undiscovered in a now alerted front line. At the count of eight I leaped up and dashed to the bunker entrance. I immediately backed out into the trench and cried "Burning!" the prearranged warning that the explosion was imminent. Meanwhile I held my automatic pistol aimed, and not a moment too soon. A fraction of a second before the explosion, directly after I had hurled the charge, a Russian appeared at the entrance. I shot at him, he fell back into the bunker. I just had time to drop to the bottom of the trench, stop up my ears and open my mouth when the explosion came. It was a terrific concussion. The entire bunker with its three men, the machine gun and the ammunition blew up in a thousand pieces. The blast pressure was like a blow over the head, and I was half stunned. Then followed the disgusting smell of powder, and pieces of beams, earth and stones rained down upon us. Scarcely had the first dust and smoke cleared when I was up again. Out of my breast pocket I pulled two rifle grenades, twisted off the caps and pulled the fuses. I was back at the bunker, now a heap of beams and mud. Opposite it, the door to the dugout had been partly blown out and inside I heard voices. I threw the grenades in there, again yelled my warning, but now ran in the direction of Kampmann's group at the right. I heard the first shout from there. "Klaus," Hugo came dashing toward me, "did you get any prisoners?"

"I? Not one. All dead. I thought you..."

"All I've got are two dead Russians. We'd better get out of here."

"Okay. Shoot your whistling catridge and we'll meet in the hollow."

We both ran back to our groups and I ordered our immediate retreat. We had to use the few minutes of confusion in order to get out of the wire and mine field. The shots, the cries, the explosion had, of course, alerted the Russian front. By the light of pale magnesium flares, we found the lane in the Russian wire and ran back to the hollow. Scarcely had I hurled myself into the mud there, as the last in my group, when the Russians let go with everything they had. From all sides, around us and over our heads, the missles hissed, zoomed and howled. Why the devil didn't I hear the whistling grenade which was suppose to give our artillery the signal to surround us with fire and cover our retreat?

Schmidt's group and a few of Kampmann's men were just disappearing into the hollow on their way back to the palisade. "Where's Hugo?" I called to the last man. "Right behind me," he yelled. I sent everybody on except Wallerstein. All hell now broke loose. There was no need for our artillery to hold back any longer, and our grenades howled over our heads into the Russian trench and beyond. This stopped the Russian infantry weapons, but now the trench mortars were hurtling their dangerous burden at us. Wallerstein and I were still lying in the hollow waiting for Hugo. In despair I must have shouted his name fifty times into the tattered night and into the inferno of bursting shells. I knew I had to go after Kampmann. He must have left the Russian trench, so he must be lying somewhere in the area of the immediate front. I motioned Wallerstein to lie still and pushed myself back in the direction of the Russian trench. It was insane. I was weeping with helplessness or fear or rage or despair. And somehow I was hoping for a miracle.

It *was* a small miracle. After about fifteen meters I found him at the edge of the mine belt, fifteen meters in front of the wire. His chest was shattered and half his face was gone. With a last burst of strength I pulled the half-naked corpse into the hollow. Wallerstein came to my aid and, each of us tugging one leg, we had to push our way close to the ground while the shells crashed all around us. Later, two medical orderlies came crawling up with a stretcher. I was the last man to squeeze through the hole in the palisade. The commander was waiting there. He took my arm and together we ran to the nearby bunker.

There I sat, trembling with exhaustion and fright, and weeping a little.

"Drink this, Heck; it'll calm you. You did very well. Here." He fumbled with his decorations. "Here is the Iron Cross 1st class for your achievement. You deserve it and it will come in handy at the officer's training school. We shall not forget that you brought back our Kampmann under these circumstances. We shall mourn his death, but that is war. He gave his life for all of us. He was a good comrade."

I sat there numbed, and as in a dream I heard the others congratulating me. I thought of Hugo, lost control of myself and wept. The commander was embarrassed and left.

The next morning we went over it all once more. Schmidt's group had actually halted after discovering the mines and remained lying there until we returned. Kampmann's group, like mine, had pushed forward into the trench, but was discovered by a Russian who, after a brief cry, was silenced by a pistol shot. This ended Hugo's chance of bringing in a prisoner. His group had then combed the trench in both directions and killed another Russian. At that point Hugo and I had met and started back.

Hugo's whistling catridge had failed and he had none in reserve. He was the last of his group to dash through the wire. He must have been shot in the heel and fallen with his chest against a mine.

Thus, the record read: Assault Troop Kampmann. Mission: Destroy machine gun replacement and bring in prisoners. Result: Machine gun emplacement destroyed. About seven Russian dead. No prisoners. Our casualty: One ROB non-commissioned officer dead.

That same morning came the order: Heck to Pleskov to the general. From there to be shipped home to officers' training school. Probationary period at the front ended.

I packed my belongings, said goodbye and walked through the swampy wood to the regiment to pick up my papers for the Iron Cross, 1st class. They had not been signed, and I could not wait. I gave back the commanders' decoration, and that was the last I was to hear of my regiment. In Pleskov I was introduced to the general. A brief handshake and congratulations. I marveled at the enormous concrete bunker. Then off to the railroad station. In the train I had plenty of time to digest everything.

I realized that my immediate future would bring months of training. Perhaps the war would be over then? I remembered what Captain Suck had said; I thought of home and my family. So far we had all come through.

But home had become a nightmare. The large cities lay in ruins. Hundreds of thousands had perished in the flames and the bomb explosions. Worn and exhausted, everybody seemed to be living on their final reserves of strength. Even in the small towns there was terrible misery. The city-dwellers had fled there from their bombed-out homes and were living in cellars and attics. French prisoners were working side by side with the farmers; in the factories there were brigades of foreign workers. Party slogans were painted on all house walls, and people, even friends, were uncommunicative and mistrustful. Was there no way out of this war? Would the miracle weapons be employed and bring about a change?

At this time the flying bombs, or V-1s, were used for the first time against England. We all listened. Was this the turning point? Vindication for Hamburg, Cologne, our beautiful cities. We heard the reports over the BBC, though this, too, was strictly forbidden. And then I thought of my division in Russia and realized that the war would not be won with the V-1s.

On July 1, 1944, I started my training school in Metz. Glad to have escaped the problems at home, I concentrated on my officer training. There was a fresh, open spirit among us cadets. Open in so far as we all discussed the general situation very critically; there were no braggarts and propagandists. The officer instructors obviously were making an effort to keep political arguments to a minimum. Our commander, Colonel Tollsdorf, an East Prussian, who wore the knight's cross with the gold wound stripe, was an imposing personality. Among my chums were two whom I remember well; one was Werner Dahl, with whom I became friends; the other was Lawrence, whom I should have liked to know better but who was reserved, or rather, somewhat snobbish.

We seldom had a chance to go out to Metz; our duties were quite strenuous. Sometimes we marched through the old section of the city, and our part-songs resounded to our dashing cadence step. At such a moment one's heart beat faster, and one was proud to be a soldier. The

citizens were undoubtedly of a different opinion; there was a sign of friendliness to Germans. Hitler had once promised the people of Alsace-Lorraine that he would not draft their sons. But here, too, he must have changed his mind, for in my division in Russia the medical-officer aspirant had come from Metz. However, I loved Metz and kept looking for the fictional characters of the Mungenast* stories. I corresponded about this with the author who, himself a native of Lorraine, would have liked to see that country form a bridge between the nations.

About this time I became acquainted with Annette, the young Frenchwoman with the Lorrainese father. With her I spent the few free hours that my duties permitted. I was terribly in love, and if there had been more opportunity I should probably have given up some of my bedroom principles for her.

Mother also came to visit me; I shall never forget the wonderful time we had and our walks through the parks of Metz.

Two significant events occurred at this time. First, the beginning of the allied invasion of France. No one was optimistic about the result. We had hoped that the Atlantic Wall would not let the attackers through, but then we thought of that time in Denmark, where the huge bunkers were insufficiently manned, the supply of ammunition and fuel miserable and the citizens at our backs hostile. No, I was scarcely surprised at the fiasco. However, we personally were still on the safe side, nor did we have much time to worry.

Even more startling was the second event, the news of the attempted assassination of Hitler. That came as a bombshell. The first reaction was one of shock and abhorrence. Who the devil was trying to take over the leadership at this hour and stab Hitler in the back? Then we discussed what would happen if...? Himmler will take over and make a shambles of everything. Others beside me were of the opinion that Goering would be the only conceivable successor for whom even our enemies would have a certain amount of sympathy, who had connections and would perhaps be in a position to make some sort of honorable settlement.

The abortive attempt set off a wave of arrests. One heard scores of names mentioned in connection with the affair and the more one heard, the more confused one became. "The Führer himself certainly wants what is best for us, but still, there must be something terribly wrong up there." The talk about sabotage was endless; suddenly we realized that, in fact, we had two fronts, the fighting front and the one that was wearing us down at home.

The first noticeable change was the abolition of the military salute. The soldier was now obliged to raise his hand and say "Heil Hitler." This

---

*Novelist

was particularly difficult for the older officers, and any success which this measure may have had was certainly not one which the Party hoped for.

I remember one roll call in the courtyard of the barracks when we were introduced to a general of the so-called foreign armies east. This good man came to us for the purpose of rounding up officer volunteers for his Russian, Ukranian and Asiatic battalions, most of them made up of former prisoners, now in German uniform, who were spending this time fighting with us against the dread Bolsheviks. The general was obliged to leave without a single volunteer.

Meanwhile the situation at the front had changed tremendously. Patton was pushing his army forward in the direction of Chalon. The war was coming closer. We drilled day and night, usually on the field in front of the mighty old fortifications on the heights outside Metz. Here were the old battlefields of 1870-I and 1918. Here our fathers and grandfathers had fought. Hundreds of old gravestones scattered about everywhere reminded us of those times. It actually seemed as though it were now up to us to pay our tribute of blood on this same spot.

Toward the end of August, it was suddenly announced that Himmler, who had meanwhile clearly moved up to third man, taking over the police and the ministry of the interior, along with his duties as top SS leader, would personally take over command of the Metz sector, and that a final defensive action would bring the enemy to a halt. The next day we were divided into platoons, equipped with automatic pistols and ordered to a barracks on the main highway between Chalon and Metz. There, Himmler himself appeared. While his adjutant announced the details, Himmler stood in his open car and blinked at us through his spectacles. The command was: "The road will be closed. Every approaching car will be searched for soldiers. If there are soldiers in the car, regardless of rank, they will be immediately escorted to the barracks courtyard. There, their papers will be examined, authorized cases will be handled by Himmler, all others will be grouped in units and immediately transported to the front. If you encounter resistance, warn first, then shoot."

Five minutes on the highway sufficed to make us understand and welcome the command. The hodgepodge of refugees fleeing eastward from the front was unbelievable. German privates with entire households, including French girls; officers with cases of champagne; moving vans from Paris; vagabonds, half of them in civilian clothes, a caravan of dodgers, refugees, marauders, drunks; an entire brothel complete with pimps—a mad assortment.

They were stunned by our efficiency and the name of Himmler. One general threatened to shoot us—he soon had an opportunity to explain to Himmler the reasons for his flight. He disappeared a short time later in a truckful of privates going back to the front. Two days later we were relieved by SS men and marched back to our barracks.

It was August 31st. We were wakened at midnight and ordered to fall in line in the courtyard. By the light of a lantern, we heard the voice of our new commander (Tollsdorf had returned to his unit on the eastern front):

"By order of our Supreme Commander, our Führer Adolf Hitler, you are herewith raised to the rank of officers. You have all become lieutenants in the reserve of the greater German army. I congratulate you and ask you to raise your right hand and repeat after me the oath of the Führer and to the fatherland."

We repeated the oath.

The night was clear, stars shone down into the dark barracks yard with its long shadows. Our hearts beat faster. Officer! What a responsibility, what a duty! Germany, the fatherland were my first thoughts. Then it came to me in a flash that my youth was being snatched from under me. I was not only grown up now, but I was an example, a leader, a representative of a highly esteemed caste which appealed only to tradition, a sense of duty, commitment and sacrifice. Not one of us thought of risking his life for the Party, for the Third Reich, for race or superman priority. The subsequent personal handshake of our commander with each one of us must have shown him eyes that were full of good will, of readiness to set an example and, if necessary, die for Germany.

After this roll call there was an announcement. We were asked whether anyone was ready at this point to volunteer for service as lieutenant in the Waffen SS, division "Goetz von Berlichingen." This opportunity was open to us as a result of a shortage of leaders and was not tantamount to incorporation in the SS. We had an hour's time to think it over and discuss it in our rooms. We realized that the Waffen SS represented an important unit. It was well known that they had the best equipment and were made largely of volunteers. All of them were between the ages of eighteen and twenty-two. SS troops were thrown in at crucial points; they fought superbly and were then put in a stand-by position. All this, of course, had its advantages. I had only to think of my garrison. What I saw there in the way of reserves was pitiful: average age thirty-five, all men with families, many with all kinds of ailments, tired and emaciated. What could one do with these men in combat?

Nevertheless, I could not volunteer; and only a handful of the others volunteered for the SS.

Within the hour, we set to work sewing on our new army officer epaulets. Lawrence even produced an officer's cap out of his locker. Another man conjured up a bottle of cognac, and we all drank out of one glass. In the middle of our celebration came the sudden order: Prepare for combat action! Two hours later we were on the march. We formed platoons with the oldest lieutenant the platoon leader. I lugged a machine gun on my shoulder. During our march, piecemeal explanations came through. We were told the Americans were advancing on Metz. We would be thrown into battle, the entire training school. The night was long and we marched and marched.

I am fond of the hilly landscape of Lorraine with its plum orchards and its isolated farms. They always have gray stone walls, wrought-iron gates, buildings with small windows. Everything has an aura of the past; it is not amusing, colorful, gay, but rather dignified, reserved, proud and sad. I should have loved to go into one of the farmyards and talk to the people, learn about them and tell them about us. The longer we marched into the morning, the more refugees we met. It seemed the peasants here were retiring into the hills and woods in order to make way for the onrush of the war. This could not have been anything unusual for the people here; generations of them had lived through it: Germans come, Germans go, French come, Americans come and go. Someone will always be coming, and their homes will certainly suffer. They have prepared for it. They go into the woods and while they are waiting, they have liaison agents who keep an eye on the villages. They leave doors and cupboards open, knowing that a soldier will break open a locked door. Valuables are usually buried in prepared hiding places. The best linen is put into full bathtubs where it is perfectly safe; who wants to cover himself with a wet sheet?

Little villages through which we marched were already evacuated. The Americans would not be far off. In the distance we heard the boom of artillery. From the heights near Gravelotte we descended into the Moselle Valley. The platoons separated.

Toward noon we rested on the Moselle highway, near the ruins of a Roman aqueduct. I sat down on the edge of the road with Werner Dahl and we ate our sandwiches. The sun was shining; it was so peaceful. A small, slow plane was hopping over the wooded hill in front of us. What a life they have, our brothers of the air force. By the way, that one up there doesn't look at all like a German liaison plane. That could almost be ...

Suddenly, out of a clear sky, shells rained down upon us. I just managed to leap into the ditch when six shells burst around us and along the roadway. I raised my head. A cloud of dust was still hovering over the ground. It was deathly quiet. I called over: "Come on out, Werner old boy, they certainly don't love us!" I looked along the ditch. The dust had yielded to wind and sun. All was the same as before. All but Werner. A few steps beyond, he was lying in the same ditch and not moving. My heart pounded as I ran over to him. It seemed to miss a beat when I looked at his chest. Where his heart should have been there was a gaping hole in his uniform, out of which dark red blood flowed into the ditch. I grasped his hand, still warm. His eyes were wide open, staring glassy and strange into the blue sky. Stunned, I tottered over to the little house where the rest of the men were just coming out to see what those shots had meant. I told them Werner was dead. Nobody could believe it. I myself refused to believe it. But there it was. There was no further shot. Werner was carried to Metz that night and buried there. For us, the battle of Metz had begun, and this time our enemies were the Americans.

Things happened thick and fast. The following days saw us in the prearranged defense positions. The Amis* pushed forward, were resisted, retreated, rounded up artillery and beat down upon us remorselessly. My platoon was lucky. We were stationed on a side road and had dug ourselves in well. We had received our baptism of fire, but after that we had not seen any Amis for days. Nevertheless, we lost two men, and their loss affected me as much as that of Werner.

The two were Lawrence and Schneider. They presumably lost their way on a bicycle patrol from Fort Manstein to Mars sur Moselle. The next morning bicycles were found in the ditch by the roadside. We never heard anything more of the two. I should have liked to discuss the incident with other friends who knew Lawrence, but that same day we were all shuffled around and reassembled in various units of the training school. Nonetheless, I kept thinking that the disappearance of the two pointed to a possibility that would have been absurd on the eastern front. It was the possibility of defection. The English name "Lawrence," of course, brought it to mind, but I may have been mistaken. When I think back now, I must say that I and probably most of the men I knew would not have been capable of defection here or elsewhere.

Dear Mamma,

Place unspecified **
September 18, 1944

Yesterday I received your letter of September 9th. You must not worry too much. Things are all right with us. The situation is, of course, getting more critical by the hour, but everyone is putting his faith in the weapon which must finally come for us. If not, we've lost this war. At the moment, I am all right. Not that I have a shelter; yesterday I got soaked, but at any rate it is quiet here. There is retreating right and left, and I imagine it will soon be our turn. Well, it will all come out somehow; we must not despair.

Love from your faithful son

Klaus

Actually, we were once more in the oppressive calm after the storm, or rather, the calm in the eye of the hurricane. For the first time since Normandy, the Americans had a firm defense belt in front of them. The local papers and army communiques were full of reports about the

---

*Pron. amees is German slang for Americans.

**My mother saved all my warletters. Without them I would not have been able to recollect all these details.

fighting of the cadet training school of Metz. Thus, the enemy had decided to stop for breath. For us this meant finding out what they were going to do next. We resorted to the old expedient of taking prisoners.

The next morning I was on my way to Gravelotte with a group and a wire rope. A road leading north from Gravelotte showed unusually heavy American vehicular traffic. That was our destination. We were allowed one day to tramp there, make our plans and come back at night with prisoners. It was a foggy, rainy day. It took us two hours to get to the road, two hours over fields and meadows; then we lay at three different places for three hours for observation. Our plan was now ready and we marched back a stretch to a lonely farm where we decided to wait until the moment of action. The courtyard was empty, but unlocked. No Amis had been here. We sat in the dark view of the single road and drank some good whiskey that one of the men had brought along. I scarcely knew the names of my comrades; like me, they were all lieutenants, all young.

"My plan," said the assault troop leader who had brought the wire rope along, "my plan may be crazy, but it'll work. At the spot we have decided upon we shall stretch the wire twelve inches above the road. On our side is the big tree. On the other side is the grave with the heavy gravestone. That's our first hurdle. We'll have to work fast. When you"— he pointed to me—"give us the light signal, we two have only a few seconds to stretch the wire and knot it. We shall then stay on the other side and wait for the vehicle. We must count on the fact that the single prisoner will be injured. Therefore, we must make a stretcher for him. We are interested only in the prisoner. We'll meet Heck here. You, Heck, as soon as you hear the accident take place will come back to this courtyard, no need to come to us. From here we shall review the situation. The Amis cannot see or reach this farmhuse from the road, even by day. That gives us the needed advantage. I want no shooting, no unnecessary noise. Your job, Heck is particularly important. You are lying half a kilometer farther down the road. You choose the vehicle. I don't want a tank or truck, I want a passenger car or a jeep. I want one single car and no traffic coming from the opposite direction. I know this may mean that we'll have to wait five hours. We have all night. Don't let anything go wrong. You'll give us a green light. Hold it so that the enemy won't see it. As soon as we see your green light, we'll block the road. If you should be doubtful at the last minute because of some unforeseen event, signal red. Then we'll have a last-minute chance to drop the wire. You two on the tree side, watch out for the red light. If you should see it, yell 'red,' nothing more. We can carry only one wounded man; if we have several, we'll take only the one who's least seriously wounded. In any case, we must tie the prisoner's hands behind his back to prevent his destroying important documents. I and I alone shall search the car for papers. Is all this clear?"

We fashioned a stretcher and toward eight o'clock in the evening, in light rain, we stationed ourselves on the spot agreed upon. There was little traffic, and almost all of it in one direction. The Amis were obviously unconcerned; their headlight dimming was lousy and I found it surprising that they did not drive in armed convoys. This was an area in which the offense had been halted; though clear defense lines had not yet been erected everywhere, the nonchalance with which they drove about in this region made us angry.

Soon everything was in readiness, and I started off to my position. Twice I had to lie down in the ditch when a car approached. Then the long vigil began. Most of the vehicles were trucks. Several jeeps came along, but then there was traffic from the opposite direction. I sometimes felt that the whole plan had a touch of bandit tactics; but, on the other hand, it was simply a rather unusual method of capturing a much-needed prisoner. The group leader was right: what would have been better—marching to Gravelotte and storming the place with six men?

There's one coming! Not too fast, a jeep. Two men inside. They've just past me. No traffic in the opposite direction. Green light. Everything O.K? I look in both directions. He's the only one. Sorry, mister.—Already I heard the crash. It was terrible, but brief. Then absolute quiet. No fire. Darkness. It's all over. I looked up and down the road once more. Not a soul. I set out for the farm where I arrived somewhat ahead of the others and quickly searched house and barn for possible surprises. Nothing. The men approached carrying a stretcher. "Where's the other one?" was my first question. "Dead." And what does this Ami look like? He was unconscious, had a few scratches on his face, otherwise no sign of injury. His hands were tide to the side of the stretcher; they would have hung limp in any case.

"We'll set out immediately and take turns carrying."

Four of us carried him which was not too difficult, and we brought him straight to Fort Manstein headquarters. He was a young, tall, thin redheaded lieutenant. We were congratulated and gazed at with a certain amount of awe; then we marched back to our positions. I never heard anything official about the prisoner. Once, someone came from headquarters and when we questioned him, he said that as far as he knew the man never woke up. However, his papers were interesting.

There was another German platoon operating in this region on the same night. They heard two more cars crash into our wreck. One of the cars was put back in shape and was now being driven by a staff major of the German army.

Soon after this incident, we were shifted around once more and soon found ourselves directly on the main highway that runs along the Moselle. My post was a shelter in the little railway station of Ars sur Moselle. In front of me, on the right, the deserted village; on the left, the tracks, a meadow and the Moselle; behind me, the road to Metz. Across the river the SS division "Goetz von Berlichingen" was fighting desperately. Our defense line ran from the river along the edge of the village in front of us, up the hill and into the woods. Now and then we were under artillery bombardment, but at first there was no sign of the attackers. We grew accustomed to sleeping during the day and being on the lookout at night. Since no provisions reached us here, we were obliged to cook for ourselves. We entered kitchens and broiled chickens, helped ourselves to canned goods and slept in our boots on beds with mattresses. Whenever anything looked suspicious, we would scurry back to our holes.

I do not know how it was possible, but one day Annette came to visit me. She brought food and drink and implored me to go with her, saying she had civilian clothes for me, that she knew a way past the Amis and that I would then be on the safe side, with her. She said the war was as good as lost for Germany; why was I so proud and stubborn not to concede it?

I was very despondent when we parted. My friends wanted to know who she was and were incredulous when I told them. In their eyes, I was a Casanova of the first water. From our point of view there was, on the one hand, besides loyalty and love of country, the thought of a turning point as a result of the miracle weapons. V-1 and V-2 were now being used and looked good to us, good enough so that we could hope for success. Moreover, there was the possibility of sudden counter-offensives in which defectors would be caught and their families at home would become the victims of so-called "clan arrests." Lawrence, I thought again, if he is on the other side, did the right thing. He was listed as missing, with the possibility of having been killed in captivity.

Annette was right; I did not want to face the truth. If she had been German—who knows? I was not ready for her proposition. We expected to be relieved within a few days. For me this would mean that I was finished in the west, perhaps finished altogether. I felt miserable and would have given a great deal to have had a real friend or my brother to talk to.

My brooding was cut short. The Amis became more lively. Things were starting up over there across the Moselle and soon we, too, were under artillery fire. Then tanks rumbled through the village. We had fifteen recoilless grenade dischargers and one machine gun. There were two of us in the concrete dugout. Our position was ideal and safe. Only a direct hit into the entrance could shake us. Our nearest neighbors lay fifty meters from us, in holes on the other side of the road. The tanks must have been one house away, but we did not see them. They stopped short of our crossing and turned off up the hill along our front line. What luck I thought, and heard the noise of motors on the Moselle. Two assault boats, each with fifteen Amis, were coming down the river. They landed 200 meters above my position. I could not see the landing place itself, but figured they must now be coming up the embankment. In one minute they were actually approaching in two groups and crossing my section of the tracks. I had all the time in the world to take up my position, calculate the distance and fire lying down. I am certain that every man in the first group was hit. The newly approaching group had not yet seen my position, and probably had no idea how badly the first group had fared, for the same thing was repeated. As far as I was concerned, it meant very brief bursts of fire and quickly I would pull my machine gun back into the bunker. They could not possibly have seen me. An artillery spotter must have sized up the situation, however, for we were suddenly covered again. About fifteen minutes went by, and the same maneuver was repeated with two more boats at the same place. I couldn't understand it. Why boats? Why here? There must have been some other reason that eluded us. About 100 meters in front of us lay dead and wounded Amis on the tracks and alongside them. Then an amazing thing happened. I heard a vehicle approach and stop, and suddenly I saw an Ami wave a Red Cross flag from behind a house wall. I could not believe my eyes. There was no further shot from the other side. I ran to the rear bunker entrance and yelled to my neighbor across the street, "Stop firing!" which he did, though evidently puzzled. Now Ami medical orderlies came with stretchers and, without paying any attention to us, started working on their casualities. They ran back and forth and dragged their men to safety. A group came within fifty meters of us. When they finished, they moved back, waved their Red Cross flag again and the little miracle was over.

That same night our group was relieved. The privates were not a little surprised to see only lieutenants here. We marched back to Fort Manstein, slept a few hours and were transported back to our barracks. Here our papers were waiting for us, along with our new officer uniforms. After a brief farewell, we all went our separate ways. I ran to Annette's house. The apartment was empty and, to my amazement, the other occupants of the building denied that this family had ever lived there. Goodbye, Annette, time—our time—has run out. Wherever you are, I wish you luck.

Here in Metz, only fifteen kilometers from the combat scene, things were quiet; the cafes were crowded and people looked at us idly and rather sardonically.

In the evening I was at home in Weinheim with my mother. I felt rather like a hero in a small circle. Photographs were taken of the swaggering soldier and I was thoroughly annoyed that my Iron Cross had never been confirmed. I had a few days of rest and anxious deliberation with Mother. It was perfectly clear that from the garrison I would be sent back to the eastern front. The thought was hard to take.

On my journey to Herford I stopped off in Cologne and Düsseldorf. The sight of these demolished cities was indescribably sad. In Düsseldorf the entire populace had been mobilized; children and old people were obliged actively to participate in the defense of the city—a senseless enterprise.

I spent two weeks in Herford. No one agreed about where the new officers were most urgently needed. Since I was thankful for every delay, I quickly accepted the offer of a five-weeks' course as company commander. The two weeks in Herford were a joke. First I became head of a so-called stomach battalion, then an ear battalion. These are units made up of unfit men suffering from stomach and ear ailments. The stomach men were scarcely able to walk and could not carry anything. In the morning I would march them to a meadow and let them all relax while I attended to my mail. With the ear men, most of whom maintained they could hear nothing, I practiced finger and sign language. I wrote out an official request suggesting that these men be sent home where they could be more useful. The document was not even accepted; the adjutant suggested that I keep my wisdom to myself and concentrate on my front duty. As he spoke, he poured lavender toilet water on his handkerchief and dabbed his forehead with it. Ever since, the smell of lavender toilet water has nauseated me.

It was now announced that the company commander course would be given in Arys in East Prussia, and I was relieved to leave Herford. The long trip to East Prussia was frequently interrupted by air attacks. Arys seemed to me the lousiest hamlet on earth. But, after all, what was Arys to me! The barracks compound and the training fields were the same as everywhere. There was one difference: we were all officers and I was the youngest. The drill was strict, but endurable. The head of the school, Colonel Becker, was more than strict and scarcely endurable. Later, I had the honor of a personal encounter with him. But first I must mention my affair with the only girl on the training field of Arys.

I relate the episode merely to give a picture of my immature, searching, expectant and irresolute self. The girl's name was Erica. She was the daughter of the barracks attendant and possibly the only female creature far and wide. She was 17 or 18, pretty and the roguish type. Where and how I made her acquaintance is beside the point. Suffice it to say, she seemed to like me and was only too willing to accept my invitation for brief, clandestine strolls. I was not in love or deeply impressed, and I was perfect aware that she was easily attracted. One evening, I asked my only roommate if he would mind going to the movies; I felt like taking a rest in our room. His eyebrows went up and there was a sullen expression around his mouth. I begged him not to fish around for explanations, whereupon he became the perfect gentleman, wished me luck and departed. Shortly thereafter two "men" whisked up the stairs, down the corridor and into my room. I helped her out of my coat which was much too long for her. Our hearts were pounding and soon I switched off the light.

For years I was known as an expert in the theory of the art to make love, but no one knew that, despite all my affairs, I had never yet broken my resolution to go to bed with a girl only if we truly loved each other. Not that I boasted about it; I kept it strictly to myself. With Erica I made up my mind to break this resolution, obeying my need rather than my true impulse. Things outside seemed to be moving toward the end; the prospect of dying without ever having possessed a woman threw a pall over me. Love gives meaning to life and not to have experienced this essential part of love seemed dreadful to me as I faced the possibility of the end. Erica, I told myself, is an uncomplicated girl, let's hope a somewhat experienced one, to whom I need not make false promises, who knows the difference between a casual affair and real love. But what I experienced now had never occurred in my erotic fantasies, namely, that love-making is an art that must be learned, a technique which, if lacking, can render the novice powerless to steer full sail ahead, that is, toward his goal. I murmured something about an excruciating headache. Erica, I realize now, was just as much of a bungler.

In the midst of these cheerless pleasures, there was a sudden whispering in the corridor and a knock on our door. With one leap I was at the closet, pushed everything aside, shoved the unclothed girl into the closet, threw her clothes after her and opened the door. There stood five of my comrades. They craned their necks and looked under the bed. Naturally, they were disappointed when I assured them that I had been resting, that their suspicions were premature and so on. About an hour later Erica and I slipped hastily out of the room; for, when I finally returned with the extra coat under my arm, I was observed, but I kept my denials purposely nonchalant.

All this would have been but water under the bridge if, the following day, slight discomforts had not suddenly manifested themselves, which Neumann, the medical orderly, tried to combat with a gray salve. Since such things cannot be ignored and our course lasted another three weeks, I was obliged to face the humiliation of visiting the doctor. Shaved where no one wants to be, reeking of cuprex* and depressed, I took my cross upon myself. My friends kept a discreet silence. Erica was not questioned; in fact, I had no further opportunity of seeing her. I was disillusioned in so many respects that there is no point in dwelling on them.

An evening's entertainment was announced to mark the end of our course. In the officer's casino, all the participants were to spend a pleasant evening of music and alcohol in the company of the bigwigs. Our major spoke to me the day before. "Lieutenant Heck, I am planning to put Colonel Becker at your table tomorrow evening. I'd like you to arrange something jolly. Cheer him up a bit. I've a notion you have had experience in putting over something like that, what? Well, here's your chance!"

*Medicament against this type of hair louse.

Some chance! Colonel Becker has a face like the Matterhorn; he's known for his severity and unapproachableness. That'll be something.

The evening began. We sat at small tables in groups of six, drinking beer, a small orchestra was playing. There were, of course, no women present. Here and there, the party was getting noisy and jolly when suddenly the door opened and the major announced: "Gentlemen, the Commander."

We all rose and Colonel Becker walked briskly into the room. Dead silence. "Good evening, gentlemen." As he spoke, his knight's cross with its swords clinked softly.

"Good evening, Colonel."

"Please resume your seats."

The major brought him to our table, to the empty seat next to mine. We all stood up again like automatons, then each of us was introduced. The Colonel drank wine. Our beer glasses were immediately exchanged and wine was served. Well, I thought, as the youngest perhaps you'd better start. I grasped the stem of my glass with three fingers, held it up against my second button and said: "Colonel, gentlemen, permit me, as the youngest, to raise my glass and drink to your..."

"Sit down," the Colonel interrupted. "Gentlemen, even though we are in the midst of a grave hour, even though the most brutal of foes is at our door, nevertheless I should like you to realize that I set great store by the rules. We are here in order to learn and therefore I should like to tell you how it is done."

After he had explained the proper form in detail, he pointed to the badge on his sleeve. "Do you know what that is?"

"Yes, Colonel, that is the Demyansk badge."

"Correct. Do you also know my nickname?"

"No, Colonel," I remarked, hoping that now things would liven up a bit.

"They call me the horror of the hollow!"

I hesitated, somewhat puzzled, then burst out laughing. "How amusing!"

"Not at all amusing," the Colonel said severely.

"Oh, no, not amusing," I echoed quite seriously.

He looked at me darkly for a moment and then explained something about the hollow at Demyansk where he brought the troops, in courageous combat, back to our lines.

Then the Major said, "Colonel, I believe Lieutenant Heck has prepared a little entertainment for us."

"Ah, very nice. Let everything quiet down and then let's have it."

This was almost too much for me. Besides, my old lice bites were beginning to itch in this heat and I kept imagining I smelled cuprex.

After a flourish of trumpets and kettledrums from the orchestra, I went through my old routine: the Nuerburg Ring. I played the sports announcer in an auto race, describing the entire atmosphere and giving the background of motor sounds, martial music and cheering of the masses. It always went over big when I imitated Goebbel's nasal voice or played Robert Ley thanking Hitler for reduced tickets for the workers. It was all very ironical but not politcally malicious. As always, it was a huge success. When I saw the Colonel laughing until the tears came, I felt a certain satisfaction. He then took me aside and warned me to be careful with such presentations; there were too many people, he said, who might put the wrong interpretation on them and cause me trouble.

It was early December when I was finally on my way to the front. I was ordered to the Volksgrenadier division 1061. The high number told me that this was a new unit, presumably made up of the last reserves of men and material. My journey led me straight through East Prussia to Poland, to the River Narev between Novgorod and Lomsha. The last letter from home brought good news. In the Reinerz Spa in Silesia Mother had met Hans who was able to spend a brief furlough there. Thus, our family had come through these years sound and well. For Mother it must have been dreadful to know that both her boys were now infantrymen on the eastern front.

When the military Volkswagen set me down at the command post of the division it was bitter cold and deep snow lay in the sparse grove. I was put in the guest bunker and ordered to have supper with the General. The elderly, good-looking Major General of the reserves was sitting at the table with three officers. Candlelight made the table look festive. The room had log walls, was unusually large for a bunker chamber and had an atmosphere of comfort. The food was simple and good. The conversation was limited to generalities. It turned out that the General had known my father well and was deeply impressed by him. This, of course, made me feel good, for it was the thirteenth anniversary of my father's death. The General then mentioned my unit. He wished me luck, told me there was a shortage of officers and that I would have to realize I would probably be the youngest in my battalion; the average age was over thirty-five and the men were not well trained. Only model behavior on my part would give me the proper authority.

The horse-drawn sleigh took me from here to the regiment, where I was introduced to the Commander, and thence to the battalion. the name of the place was Weliki-luky. The few Polish huts had partially collapsed; the population had disappeared. The battalion bunkers were built deep into the earth. My new chief was Captian Reichenbacher from Vienna. He was good-looking and spoke with the agreeable Viennese accent. He led me to my bunker which I shared with his adjutant. Ulli Hoffmann was a talented chap; he was younger than I and we immediately became friends. Our helper, Marek, was a gem; he cared for us like a royal servant.

I was given the post of a special missions staff officer with jurisdiction over munitions, trench-digging, communications, subsequently even NSFO, of which I shall speak later. I was given a magnificent white horse.

Our living bunker was wood-paneled. We had a radio, a tablecloth, pictures on the walls, books. The food was good, and there were frequent nips of brandy. In short, it was unbelievably comfortable. The front was absolutely quiet; not a shot fell. We were 500 meters from the first line. The Russians lay 600 meters from our line. In between ran the Narev which was freezing over.

With anxiety we listened to the radio reports. We seemed to be cut off here. Battles were raging on our right wing. East Prussia was turning into a huge caldron, and we were trapped. I frequently visited the men in the front line; they were all embittered; they had all lost enough and were waiting for the end with horror. They were dead tired, for our section was huge and we did not have enough men. I myself had a wonderful life and spent every free moment on horseback.

Christmas was drawing near. We made all sorts of preparations for it, and when the day came we had an avalanche of presents to distribute. The privates were brought back in groups. The front was absolutely quiet; it was, as we all knew, the calm before the storm. 1944 was drawing to a close. We knew that no miracle weapon would save us, no single victory, no matter where, would turn the war in our favor. We were embittered and disappointed. All we hoped was to get out of the mess alive, back to Germany. But the Russians were breaking into Germany. It was like looking into the eye of the snake. Helplessness made us numb and defensive. We had no choice.

At twelve o'clock on New Year's eve I stood on a hill in the bright moonlight and looked over to the Narev, to the Russians. We must prevent these hordes from pushing into Germany, our home. The war must end now, before it is too late. Damn it all, what *is* the matter with Hitler? How can this go on? I thought of my brother who was also sittng somewhere here in the cursed east, facing Ivan. We simply must manage to get back alive. We will! And during the next few days and weeks our fate will be sealed.

Chapter Five
1945

A new year had dawned; there was no doubt that it would be the last of the war. Survival was our one thought. How it would all end was the question.

During the first few days of January we were given an order that was as unrealistic as it was amusing. Each unit, down to the battalion, was to appoint an NSFO, a National Socialist Guidance Officer. He was to be politically irreproachable and was to indoctrinate the troops in the spirit of the Party. When Reichenbacher read the order aloud to us we howled with laughter.

"Heck, do you have MEIN KAMPF?"

"Sure thing, here in the bookcase, but I've never read two pages of it."

"Well, from now on you're NSFO—in case somebody should ask!"

"Clear as mud."

And that settled a matter that had caused so much agitation, fear, panic and informer tactics in the army. For us here it was so meaningless and superfluous that it was not even worth talking about.

A week later a telephone call from the regiment announced that a Reich speaker was about to visit us. A Reich speaker was a Party man in brown uniform who dashed around the country edifying, arousing, enlightening, lining up and victimizing the unsuspecting populace and selling it down the river. These benefactors of humanity were also known as golden pheasants. We were amazed that such a bird had found his way to our front. He came in a horse-drawn sleigh and over his Party uniform he wore a sheepskin coat of absolutely gigantic proportions. He had difficulty climbing down the steps of our bunker without getting caught in it. When he had peeled off this fur, he turned out to be thin, old and ugly. He said he had a desire to bring the spirit of Hitler into the foremost trench and relight the torch of idealism. He became furious when we refused to order some of the men to come here to the battalion to listen to one of his talks. Our men were overtired and we had no reserves. After a cup of tea, he consented to set out with me to the front and speak to the men there.

It was thirty minutes through deep snow to the main battle line. The old man puffed and perspired in his sheepskin. In the trench he had difficulty stooping over, so that it was not surprising that Ivan saw us and was soon spattering us with trench mortars. I just managed to shove him into a bunker where he had such a fit of coughing that the last sleeping *Landser* woke up and looked about inquisitively.

When I introduced the old man as a Reich speaker, several of the men turned over and immediately started snoring again. He grew furious and demanded more attention. This simply goaded the men on. One *Landser* asked whether he might borrow the sheepskin for guard duty. The old man seemed on the verge of a stroke, complained bitterly and held me responsible, as NSFO. I kept nodding my head in agreement. He refused to climb around any more trenches, so I took him back to the battalion. When we gazed after his departing sleigh, we were uncertain whether to laugh or cry. We shrugged and went back to our radio in the bunker, hoping against hope that something would happen—something better than Ardennes, better than V-1 or V-2. We hoped for a miracle that would never come.

The days and nights crept endlessly by. Nothing happened, at least not in our unit. We were sitting in a dead angle. The Russians had encircled East Prussia and we were caught in the trap. On the one hand, we could be thankful that we did not have to fight; on the other hand, we knew it would be better to be near home when the end came. Here we were caught deep in the heart of Poland.

During the early days of January I took over the sixth company at the front. My division was large, the company small: fifty-five and a first sergeant. I made the acquaintance of my men, mourned my white horse, my lovely bunker and Ulli. The position was along a wooded rise, a so-called forward-slope position. Below us was the frozen Narev and 500 meters beyond, in the brush, lay the Russians. If they should approach with tanks, the ice would crack. This gave us a feeling of security.

On January 18th I was on my way from my bunker to the battalion at an ungodly hour. A company leader conference had been scheduled for six o'clock. It was a forty-five minute walk, and still pitch-dark, when I arrived in my old bunker, tired and panting because of the deep snow, and with my face burning. As usual, the room was overheated and we had to peel off our winter garments. It was good to see all the officers and old acquaintances again. The officer of the regiment was looking important and Reichenbacher had on his best uniform. He lost no time in coming to the point.

"We shall retreat, or rather, systematically withdraw. This afternoon at five o'clock everyone will leave his position unobserved; the companies will gather here at the battalion from where we shall set out on the long march. Our goal will be the area around Kreutzburg. In other words, we'll be going due north to East Prussia. The artillery is already retreating; our heavy infantry weapons will soon follow. All excitement is to be avoided in the trench. A small combat group will remain behind until we are all underway. Company six will be the last and Lieutenant Heck the rear officer. Stay together on the march and help one another! We have no cars, no vehicles; anyone falling behind cannot count on help. It will be difficult. Whatever happens, we'll see each other in Kreutzburg. Good luck!"

We sat together a while longer and discussed the details. Then we bundled ourselves into our winter uniforms once more and as we took leave of one another the sky was turning red and the dark nocturnal clouds were giving way to the dawn.

At this very moment hell broke loose. Russian artillery was firing at our foremost positions. An unbelievable barrage was tearing the early morning into shreds.

"Keep your position until five o'clock; then withdraw as agreed," Reichenbacher yelled as we ran in all directions to our various companies.

Somehow, I felt a release. It had started! No more stagnant waiting. The end had come. I ran panting through snow, my heart pounding like mad. Will Ivan attack my section? Shall we be in a position to hold him back until five o'clock?

The shells were now whistling over my head, which meant the Russians had lengthened the range of fire. Shells were hitting our battalion. Wood and hill protected me from enemy observation and I ran to the edge of the wood. There I fell exhausted into the snow and caught my breath. The men were inexperienced, I kept thinking; there are only a few veterans in my company; the rest are replacements, the last conscription, average age thirty-five. The firing now ceased and dense clouds of smoke rose from my section. To the left of me, in the snow bank, Momberg was getting the range with his six howitzers. On the right, our medium gunners were also becoming active and, finally, machine gun sheaves and rifleshots were whistling around my ears. I set out again. As I ran panting past the gunners, I realized that they were about to lay off. I ran the hundred meters toward them and it was only then that my glance fell on the thin strip of woodland—and my heart skipped a beat: Russians, Russians, hundreds of them, had broken through my company section. They're coming, Klaus; the end is approaching; the end is here. To the right I saw Sergeant Hagemann with a group of privates. We approached each other, breathless.

"Lieutenant, this is the remainder of the first and second platoon. The left wing has been penetrated; we still have contact with the right, but...heavy losses, observer positions are all lost."

He looked at me questioningly—shall we disengage ourselves? I took the remaining handful of men and built a new line here on the edge of the wood. An observer from Momberg's infantry howitzers turned up and already we were firing like madmen at the approaching Russians. A *Landser* announced that a company of reinforcements was coming from the direction of the battalion. That made it clear to me that the breakthrough had occurred only in my section. The Russians were now lying low and digging into the snow. Soon I saw the reinforcements take their position on the level of the infantry howitzer stand. I waited a while and then withdrew to that point with my handful of men. Here, to my relief, Ulli appeared. But then it started up here too.

Momberg's howitzers shot at a hundred meters in direct fire at the charging enemy lines. At the left, close combat developed. Suddenly I had a machine gun around my neck. I saw the gun limbers coming forward. The heavy bodies of the horses were steaming and rearing up. Momberg gave his orders calmly and briefly. He resembled a commanding general. The whole thing looked like a painting of a battle scene from the age of Frederick the Great. A short time later, the howitzers were out. The wounded were being dragged to the rear, down the snow-filled brook hollow. A shell had hit directly beside me. Hagemann screamed. His right arm was lying severed in the snow. Horrified, we both stared at the white, uninjured hand lying in the snow. My first impulse was to pick it up, but then I followed him as he tottered into the hollow where I bandaged the upper arm stump. Hagemann was as white as a sheet. Four years on the eastern front, and now it had to hit him. He said he had no pain.

The Russians stopped their charge. Expecting to become entirely surrounded by the enemy, we took up a defense position which we occupied until five o'clock.

When we gathered at the battalion headquarters, I was finally able to count my men: twenty-seven out of fifty-five. It was difficult to determine who had fallen, who was missing or had been taken captive. I had only twenty-seven men left; I felt like weeping. Reichenbacher tried to comfort me.

It had already grown dark as we set out on the long march. My group was the last to go. We were lucky! The Russians did not seem to have observed our departure. Goodbye, old Weliki-luky, goodbye, comfortable bunkers. We passed the place where our supply train stood, beside the regiment. Everything deserted, empty, a bit of rubbish lying about. It was pitch-dark. The rear guard soon caught up with us. Now I was the last German soldier to march into the East Prussian caldron. The units spread apart more and more; the ones ahead were growing weary. No one said a word. Everyone knew that staying behind meant death. The Russians would not capture a single exhausted soldier. And the march had just begun.

It was endless and merciless. It took all the strength I had to stumble on, but that was not enough. One man lagged behind, another fell exhausted into the snow-filled ditch beside the road. It was my task to comfort and encourage them. I advised them to creep into a hiding place, rest up and then follow us. But even I did not believe what I was saying. They would soon be discovered by the Russians, and since they were too weak to be captured, they would be finished.

Once, we succeeded in attaching a child's sled to a caterpillar tractor of the artillery that had fallen behind. This dream lasted for five kilometers, then the monster stopped—no more gas. A hand grenade tossed into the motor and an ugly heap blocked the road.

We had now crossed the border and were in East Prussia, in Germany. The villages were deserted. A few dogs were howling in the cold, clear night and now and then we heard the mooing of an unmilked, abandoned cow. In the middle of a brief halt we were overtaken by Russian tanks. Mounted with soldiers, they rumbled through the village at top speed. We hid and the nightmare was soon over. But it meant that they were at our heels.

Hours later an icy snowstorm blew up. We crossed railroad tracks. A freight train was standing there with open cars. One of the men called me to come and look. If only I hadn't! But it was no use; it was all part of the end: hundreds of frozen corpses of women and children were huddled together on the death train. They were half covered with snow; not a sound, everything was rigid. In sudden flight, they must have seen a last possibility in this open train. For all of them this white hell must have turned into heaven. On the school knapsack that one little boy clutched in his stiff hand was written the name "Friedmann Koch" in gold letters. I shall tell about you Friedmann; I was unable to protect you, as we had pledged to do. We had all been beaten but could not give up, for unconditional surrender was demanded of us. Unconditional surrender meant suicide. So we had to go on to the end.

It was getting dark again; I tottered after the others. Perhaps the war is already over and we do not know it. After all, we are here in Germany. It is already five past midnight. What does it mean: to the end? To the last cartridge? I had perhaps thirty cartridges left. And then what? To the last drop of blood? A child could knock me over now. If only we had a radio. If only we had something to eat. If only we could lie down and sleep.

I met a farmer who told us incredible horrors about the Russians. Advance detachments had been here when the population was on the point of departure. He was the only one left. His family was killed, he was able to escape, but he wanted to stay here, come what may.

Suddenly there was a standstill. Reichenbacher gathered together the battalion. Hastily we were brought into position on the road, and already Ivan was attacking. We shot like mad and kept the position. There were losses on both sides. Day dawned and the rockets became fewer. In the distance, the boom of heavy artillery. Ulli came to me and said we were cut off and alone. We must see that we get to Kreutzburg. Kreutzburg became a ray of hope, a goal—the last? We assembled and stumbled on. In a village we found the rest of the battalion. We learned that the regiment was just around the corner, the division but a stone's throw away. There was a sudden milling crowd of privates and officers. We counted our men. I had set out on the long march with twenty-seven. I had sixteen left. The rest were dead or in the hands of Russians.

Reichenbacher assigned our roles. Three companies were to take up positions at once; my group would be battalion reserves. Five minutes later we were asleep on the wooden floor of a farmhouse. The village was deserted, the houses open, the barns filled with animal stock: sixty cows, one-hundred pigs. Rich farms, poor farmers. I slept like a dead man.

The next morning we took five prisoners, young, healthy Russians who glanced about fearfully and were silent. Guards took them to division headquarters. Five hours later the guards returned with the prisoners. The division had allegedly neither room for nor need of prisoners.

"What's this nonsese?" Reichenbacher said and reached for the telephone. He spoke briefly, but listened a long time, his face registering anger, then seriousness. He hung up and turned to me.

"Heck, let the prisoners disappear and relay the message forward that we have no use for prisoners."

"What do you mean by 'disappear,' Captain?" I asked.

A master sergeant interrupted and said, "I'll take over the case, Captain," and motioned to the desperate-looking Russians to come with him. They guessed what was going on.

"You'll take over nothing," I said angrily, my heart pounding. Reichenbacher did not say anything, looked out of the window and started cleaning his pipe.

"I have nothing more to say, Klaus," he finally murmured.

I motioned to the Russians and one of my men to follow me. We crossed the farmyard, entered the big barn where a door led to the potato cellar. The Russians were talking excitedly among themselves, and before we descended the long stone steps one of them, pointing to himself, said: "Comrades, soldiers, nix Communist. Stalin nix gudd, Woyna nix gudd!"

I knew what he wanted to say; I knew that they were expecting to die and were desperately seeking a way out. With my pistol in one hand, a candle in the other. I went down the steps behind them. A bin of laths enclosed a mountain of potatoes. The little window in the high vaulted ceiling could not be reached. I motioned to the Russians to enter the bin and I explained to them in sign language and slow speech that I was going to lock them in with wire, that I was leaving a guard on the steps and ordering him to shoot if they should attempt to escape. I told them that we would move on soon and that when they heard Russian voices they could consider themselves free. They were pale and grave and nodded their heads. I went upstairs with my soldier, and our prisoners remained behind in the dark. I had a pot of potatoes cooked for them and taken down to them with a large side of bacon. The next day we moved on. Reichenbacher never questioned me, and I never mentioned the Russians again.

The following day we reached the area around Kreutzburg. Immediately the dwindling companies were assigned new positions. My men and I remained with Reichenbacher. We were lying on the edge of a village. Half a kilometer beyond was a farm, the front line. It was quiet and we were finally served the first hot meal in twelve days. We found a radio. On the western front the Allied troops were pushing against the Rhine. In the east, the Russians were already at the Oder and outside Danzig. East Prussia was thus practically cut off. Tilsit and even Gumbinnen, my grandmother's native city, had fallen. In the northeast, the circle around the Courland army, my old division in the Baltic states, was being squeezed together by the Red army.

January 30th, the twelfth anniversary of Hitler's accession to power. The radio announced that he was celebrating it among his loyal band of followers in Berlin, while the city was preparing for the siege. There was talk of *Volkssturm*, the last conscription of old people and children for the defense of what merciless bombers had left behind. Fritsche, the government speaker, was again raving about the coming miracle weapons. He also made a big thing of the transfer of Hindenburg's remains from Tannenberg to Berlin. The situation on the eastern front was now, for the first time, described as extra-ordinarily serious. Hitler spoke. His voice was deep and grave. It was impossible to resist the spell of that voice. Shivers went up my spine. He admonished all to work and to fight. He predicted the imminent final victory over England and the Asiatic hordes breaking into our country. He must know what he is doing. There must be something in it. We were sitting despondent in candlelight and discussing the situation. No one accused Hitler personally. It is the traitors surrounding him, the good-for-nothings, the generals, everything is in a perfect muddle and the Allies want only unconditional surrender. We had no answer. Despair robbed us of sleep.

Early in the morning, more shooting. From up ahead came the news that Ivan was attacking. We quickly made ready and started out into the darkness towards the farm. For a while we heard nothing but rifle shots. Then there was the rattle of tank chains. Rockets went up. And suddenly dead silence. The telephone communication was dead. Slowly the dawn rose blood-red over the nearby wood. Reichenbacher ordered my group to the farm. He had no other choice. We expected it and silently took up our weapons: a bazooka, two recoilless grenade dischargers, a few automatic pistols and, for the rest, rifles and hand grenades.

At the edge of the village we halted briefly. From here the road led straight to the farm. I gave brief orders. It was not difficult to read the faces of the men: what good is that, does it make any sense now? I was thinking the same thing. Then I looked over to the farm and thought of the men there. They were waiting for our help. Besides, orders were orders. I marched ahead and did not look back. I had gone about 100 meters when there was a loud bang and an armor-piercing shell crashed into the tree beside me. I leapt into the snow-filled roadside ditch. Three more shells burst so rapidly that discharge and crash seemed simultaneous. I waited a while and then got up and went on. Nothing mattered to me now; I marched doggedly on. There was a lull; perhaps it was not worth-while for the Russians, since I was alone. Once I turned around and yelled: "Do you want to leave our men stranded over there?" The tears came and, weeping, I stumbled on. Thus I reached the farm where I sat down in a door frame and rested. Slowly, one after the other, my men arrived. Not a sound from friend or foe. I divided the men into three groups. One group was to go into the buildings on the right, the other to go with me to the left into the barns. A few men were to remain here, among them Schultz with his bazooka. He was to cover us and follow later. I went into the cow stalls. All the cows were dead and there was not a soul to be seen. I was sweating in my winter uniform. I went out again into the barnyard. The next building was the pig barn. In order to reach it I had to run twenty meters across the barnyard entrance. I looked over to Schultz. He saw me and understood. Through the window I now saw men moving back and forth in the pig barn. Are they ours, or are they Russians? I dashed over and pulled open the door which swung outward. And here I was face to face with the end. Huge, broadshouldered with a fur cap, his pistol held in readiness. I hesitated for a fraction of a second. Was he one of ours? Then he grinned and pulled the trigger. He aimed at my abdomen. A sharp blow and I collapsed; my automatic pistol fell on the cement floor. Again he aimed quite deliberately at my abdomen. When he pulled the trigger I felt the second blow against my left hip. With all my strength I pushed myself back a few steps into the dead angle of the door. This also put me out of Schulz's range. Already his shell was zooming with incredible force against the door and the inner wall of the barn. All the windows flew out and half the barn collapsed in a welter of beams, stones, dust and powder.

Someone grasped me by the collar and pulled me back into the barn. Ulli, good to see you. So he must have followed us; he probably couldn't stand it alone with Reichenbacher. Suddenly wild shooting began. Shouts of "Hurrae" and "Hurrah" mingled with curses, racket, screams and explosions. I cautiously probed under my uniform and felt a hole in the groin. The blood was running down my legs like warm soup. I pressed a handkerchief into the wound. There was no pain; it all felt numb. Ulli was obliged to help the others. I was alone and had a minute to think.

I am without doubt seriously wounded. So this is the end. Not the end of the world, but the end for me. And if I succeed in getting out of this predicament, it will be the end of the war for me. If I don't make it back to the village, it will be the end forever. Out of this trap. Away from Ivan. Back to the village. If I manage that, I'll manage the rest: home, tomorrow, the future. I tore off all unnecessary clothing, tried to sit up, collapsed again immediately, and already I was crawling on all fours through the barn to the farmyard entrance. When I reached the road I became dizzy. I summoned my last bit of strength and crawled through the endless ditch toward the village. I must make it, I kept saying to myself. Nobody can help me. I see and hear no one.

Halfway there I met a dying soldier. He was quite yellow and asked me, his voice breaking, to give his love to his wife. I was too weak to answer and crawled on, groaning. Just before I reached the first house, I met Reichenbacher. He was lying in a snowbank, watching the farm through field glasses. He was appalled to see me in this condition and summoned two orderlies to carry me to the doctor. He wished me a final farewell: "Salute our country for me; we shall probably never see it again."

The men were carrying me to the village. I knew I would make it; for the present I was finished, but I would have a future. How to get home was secondary—I was now to experience an improbable succession of coincidences, luck and twists of fate, though from active participant I had become a passive observer. From now on I had not the faintest doubt that I would live through everything. I had regained my spirit, my sense of humor.

The men dragged me into a farmhouse where our regimental doctor had set up his first-aid station. He was very young and made a terribly awkward impression in his uniform. He spoke with a heavy Lorrainese accent. While he was examining me, we talked a little about his native city Metz. His examination had to be abruptly terminated because a new hell broke loose. "Stalin organs!" somebody shouted. They certainly had it in for us. The shells descended like rain on the few houses. We crouched in a corner and watched doors and windows burst apart. Before it was over, half the roof had caved in.

When things calmed down and the smoke had cleared, Ulli came rushing in. He had a shot through his upper arm. The doctor bandaged him up in a few minutes. Of my wounds the doctor said he could find no bullet outlets and that I would have to be transported four kilometers to the main field-dressing station. Ulli managed to get a child's sled, laid me on it and with his good arm pulled me through the snow. Our spirits mounted as we moved along and in a childishly happy mood we joked about our home-leave shots and about ourselves, the invalid veterans. Proudly I saw my Iron Cross 2nd class dangling from its ribbon. Reichenbacher had just presented me with it that morning. My first decoration had, of course, never come through.

The four-kilometer journey to the field-dressing station was hard on Ulli and, when we finally arrived, he was utterly exhausted. Hundreds of wounded were lying all the way out to the street and I do not know how Ulli managed to get me one of the few doctors. This was the last time I saw Ulli. He said goodbye and went back to the front, the doctor having told him that a clean upper-arm wound was no reason for leaving the front. Nor did he even try to leave. Ulli Hoffmann, son of a distinguished airforce general, mountain-infantryman and lieutenant, now battalion adjutant of a lost *Volksgrenadier* regiment, last officer of Reichenbacher—good luck, Ulli.

The doctor had me carried in. He removed the bandages, cleaned out the wounds and cauterized the edges.

Then he said: "You've been lucky, old man, extremely lucky. The artery here in the groin is exposed, but intact. The bullet exit is here in the buttocks. The other bullet may be lodged in the hip, let's hope not in the pelvic bone. I'll send you to Zinten to the military hospital. See that they x-ray you."

After he had bandaged me up again, two men carried me back to the street and laid me on straw in a horse-drawn vehicle. Next to me lay a private. We had not gone a kilometer when clotted blood streamed out of his mouth. He was unconscious and never woke up. We jolted on.

We met a group of refugee peasants traveling with all their possessions loaded on heavy wagons. Their numbers increased, and soon we were in the middle of a long procession of fleeing civilians. Their destination? The north, they said, then Danzig and deeper into the Reich. Somebody lifted a couple of old women onto our wagon, removed the corpse and laid it under a snow-laden fir tree. Then everything stopped. The road led through an ice-covered ford where the horses slipped and collapsed. A disastrous tangle resulted. A couple of German tanks, appearing from the opposite direction on their way to the front, cleared a detour for us and soon we were all pouring through it. Many wagons broke down and were tearfully given up, their contents reloaded or simply abandoned.

Hours later somebody cried, "The Russians are coming!" In wild panic everybody ran to the sides of the road. It was incredible. When nothing happened, everybody came back and the trek continued. A kilometer beyond we saw the catastrophe. The road was filled with the chaos of destruction. Dead human beings and animals, overturned wagons, bodies of horses crushed beneath tank chains. Everything was shoved to one side like so much rubbish and the trek of despair resumed its course. East Prussia was in flight; I dared not think where to. We reached Zinten and the hospital during the night. A nurse implored the driver not to leave me here but to take me at once to the railroad station. There stood a freight train with cattle cars, one of which was equipped with a stove and beds. We were just in time; I was scarcely in bed when the train pulled out. I tried to find out where we were going. Somebody said to Braunsberg, from there to Pomerania; the line was not yet in Russian hands. "Fine," I said and dropped off to sleep.

I was awakened by sirens. The train had stopped on an open stretch. I tried to look through a crack in the door. Suddenly low-flying planes droned above us. The bombs were already wailing. We held our breaths and clutched our beds. Crash—an explosion tossed the train back and forth. Then it was quiet. The wounded were crying for help and the soldiers in my car were calling for a doctor. Not a soul put in an appearance, and no one was in any shape to get up; everyone in the car was seriously wounded. The stove soon went out and it turned cool. I was hungry, but forced myself to get a few hours' sleep. It must have been early in the morning when I heard voices outside. Somebody yanked open the heavy door from the outside and said: "End station. The locomotive is damaged. The train isn't going any farther. You're here alone." Everybody was dumbfounded.

The man had left the door open and disappeared. It was as though someone had said lightly, yet quite seriously: prepare to die. Everyone must have felt it and, indeed, for many on this train it undoubtedly became a reality.

I dressed myself as best I could and crawled on all fours to the door. A sky full of stars, a white field, a few passing lights in the distance—that was all. Without any particular plan I heaved myself out of the car and fell into the deep snow. I crawled across the field toward the passing lights. Another day was dawning when I reached the highway, exhausted. There was not much traffic and it was all in one direction. An army vehicle picked me up. It was a personnel carrier and beside me sat a first sergeant of the air force with the German cross, a top medal for bravery. I was too exhausted to talk and soon fell asleep again.

Loud cursing woke me up. We had run out of gas and had no choice but to get out. It was then that I noticed the sergeant had only one leg. A farmer with a horse and wagon gave us a lift. A group of young people were walking along beside us and slowly I became aware that they were all talking French. I may already be slightly out of my mind, so why not try out my school French. To my astonishment, I learned that they were French prisoners who had been here for years, working for the farmers.

The flier gave me a sandwich and told me that we were on our way to Heiligenbeil where there was a large airport. He said that with his connections he could arrange to have us flown home. I thought of my brother and wondered whether he was still on the eastern front; I told myself not to worry; we'd surely make it. Itching kept me awake; the lice had crawled under my putrid bandages.

The town of Heiligenbeil resembed an ant hill. Soldiers, wounded men, prisoners and civilians were running hither and thither. In the distance, the rumbling of the front was clearly audible. Ivan could not be far from here. The farmer had to unload us opposite a church. He disappeared in a column of wagons and refugees. We sat down in the doorway of an old pharmacy. The church opposite was filled with hundreds of wounded. The poor *Landsers* were lying in long rows that extended far out into the sidewalks and streets. A few people were dishing out hot soup and feeding the weakest among them.

My flier set out for the airfield. He told me to stay where I was and he would have me picked up later. I laughed, wished him luck and hoped for the best as he hobbled off on one leg with his crutches. I waited a few hours in the doorway. Once, the door opened and two women helped me up the stairs into the apartment of the pharmacist. Here to my amazement, the large family was sitting at a festive board. They greeted me with dignity and placed me in a seat of honor at the table. They said grace and scarcely spoke throughout the meal. Even the children were pale and solemn. There were ten adults, and they ate and drank the very best of everything. Costly silver, crystal and damask were reminiscent of memorable occasions. I did not dare ask questions or even speak. When everyone was finished, the pharmacist prayed. He thanked God for the abundant life he and his family had enjoyed; he asked for help in the forthcoming difficult time. He affirmed his faith that God's will in imposing this trial on them was good, though unfathomable. Then he requested the entire family to leave everything behind, just as it was, and follow him. The doors were left unlocked. A family established for centuries said farewell to everything that had given meaning to their lives. They went out into the courtyard where two horse-drawn vehicles, packed with the barest essentials, were waiting. Thus began the flight of the pharmacist of Heiligenbeil, a flight into the unknown, a flight into the chaos of that final phase of a lost war which pitilessly lacerated East Prussia and all its inhabitants, both the good and the evil.

The family had offered me shelter in their house, but I asked to be carried back to my doorway. There I sat alone again in the ant hill and waited. The sergeant would probably come back or send me a message. The cold had abated and during the night it began to rain. The wounded in the streets now crawled into the corners of the houses and the tumult subsided. If only I had asked the pharmacist to change my bandages; the lice were driving me crazy.

A soldier appeared, shook me awake and said, "The sergeant with the amputated leg sent me to say that it's hopeless; all the planes have been destroyed on the airfield. Every day perhaps fifty-two wounded are flown in by two Ju,* but there are thousands lying on the airfield waiting. He advises you not to come to the airfield on your own. He hasn't a chance himself." While he was talking, shells burst in the distance. "That is undoubtedly out at the airport," he said; "things are about to commence

*Junckers 52 Transport plane.

in earnest there and that'll mean it's all over."

I was not too much surprised; I had not expected a miracle. The street was coming to life again. A long procession of wagons was passing through. I slid to the edge of the curb and was suddenly looking into the eyes of a young man. It was a brief moment of mutual scrutiny. He was driving a two-wheel Dockard by himself. He stopped and asked whether he could lift me up. Two minutes later I was sitting beside him. The very light, box-type cart had high wheels, and the thoroughbred horse was well groomed and prancing nervously. Behind us on packed straw was only a rucksack; it was all he possessed, he said, and his language, as well as his whole appearance, gave the impression of an aristocrat. An East Prussian Junker,* whose estates were not exactly small. We did not talk much. My wounds were painful when I sat up. When we reached Rosenberg on the Frisches Haff, the entire caravan stopped. From up ahead came the distressing message that the only escape, from here over the ice of the Frisches Haff to the spit of land and beyond, had been bombed by Russian fliers during the night. Whole columns had broken through the ice and perished. Moreover, a thaw had produced a half meter of water on the ice. Heavy vehicles, it was said, had no chance. A crossing would be possible only at night because of the constant threat of air attacks, but at night the holes and danger spots on the ice could not be seen.

Despair gripped everyone. Reloading began. In the midst of the confusion it started to rain, a nasty rain mixed with sleet. My Junker had climbed out and was talking to the group of men in the harbor. He returned and drove me over to the little basin. There he unloaded me, wished me luck, and, before I knew it, he was gone.

Here on the little quay wall a few other wounded men were lying and it seemed a good place, for in a short time a little ice-breaker towing two large covered boats emerged from the fog, rain and ice. First the wounded were lowered on a rope into the pitch-dark interior of the boats. Then followed women and children and all those who were ready to abandon all their luggage.

"We're going to be taken to Pillau!" people said. What a hopeful prospect! Pillau, the big port on the Baltic. There we'll have a chance to get on a big ship, obviously the only logical and conceivable escape. Pillau! what luck, that I should find this old boat here. Down in the dark hold it was dry and not too cold. Soon, however, the air became unbearable. The wounded were groaning, women were weeping, children whining, men cursing.

An eternity later the planks were drawn aside. We were in Pillau. The wounded were hoisted up and civilian or uniformed helpers carried them

*Aristocrat.

to a nearby surface bunker. It was one of the usual cement monsters, several stories high, with heavy iron doors and no windows. Inside, emergency lights were burning and filtered fresh air was being pumped in. I was laid in a room on the third floor. There were all kinds of people lying about. Some sat on a mountain of junk and household goods, the last wordly belongings they had salvaged. When it rained outside, the bunker became crowded. Again I heard a variety of languages. There were French and Russian prisoners among *Landsers* and civilians. No one was interested in anybody else; there was only one reason why they were all sitting here: they were waiting, waiting for a ship; a ship meant flight from the East Prussian caldron, flight from the hell that had driven us all this far to a dead end. A ship meant life; no ship meant death, violence, Siberia, starvation or laceration in the death mill of an ever-advancing front. The Russian ring around nearby Königsberg was already closed; Pillau was the next objective. Russian artillery had already begun to shell the harbor. A ship—time was running out!

I removed my winter uniform and shoved it under my head as a pillow, then I dug into my pockets for a mirror. As I felt in my little watchpocket under my belt, I touched broken fragments. I took them all out and made a curious discovery. The pistol bullet that had wounded me must have entered here. My tin identification tag, which I should have worn around my neck but carried instead in my pocket, showed a round hole. The compass with the mirror on the back was broken in a hundred pieces. The bullet must have swerved here, for the shot in the groin showed that it had struck obliquely. It must have swerved again inside, since the bullet exit in the buttocks was round and very small. I looked at my new waterproof service watch with its illuminated dial—my pride—and it showed two o'clock. I asked somebody what the date was: February 9, 1945. That was my grandmother's birthday. In 1871, the year of the war with France (we learned history according to wars), she had been born here in East Prussia. We were all so proud of our grandmother, a strong, personality, a true East Prussian. Today they would all be sitting together, thinking of me, and somehow our thoughts must meet. Your old East Prussia is lost, but your Klaus is by no means finished!

We were all hungry and anyone who managed to get hold of something to eat was regarded enviously. Now and then, someone would share a sandwich with me. Once a sailor came into the room, walked about and scrutinized the people. His glance fell upon my Iron Cross which I was still wearing. He knelt down and asked me whether he could help me.

"Bring me something to eat," I whispered. An hour later he returned with a steaming pot. Rice pudding with chocolate sauce. I was speechless. I hadn't seen anything like it since my childhood. He sat down beside me while I ate. The Navy, I thought, why must I belong to the marchers! He waited until I was finished. About five o'clock he came again and whispered into my ear, "A large hospital ship will be docking in about an hour. It will cause tremendous excitement and everybody will try to rush out. Stay here, no matter what happens. I'll come and get you. I'm the only one who can help you get on the ship. Stay here in this room."

"How do you happen to know about the ship?" I asked.

"I belong to a submarine flotilla here in the harbor. We have no fuel to go out to sea. We know about the ship through radio. Soon all of Pillau will know about it." He nodded encouragingly to me and disappeared.

Again the bunker became crowded because it had begun to rain again. Somewhat later, everyone grew restless. From below, in the hallways and on the stairs, there was a commotion. Then came the first cry, "A ship! A big ship is coming in!" Momentarily there was wild running back and forth. Everybody wanted to be the first. People gathered up their bundles and in a few minutes I was alone. A few men were taking charge of the wounded. I thanked them and said I could help myself and would be coming afterward. I began to have misgivings. Will he keep his word? He had so far. He'll come. I put on my winter jacket and waited. I gave myself an hour; after all, the big boat had to come in and dock before the loading can begin.

The hour was not yet up when I heard steps on the cement stairs. My sailor entered.

"Lieutenant, this is the situation: The ship is in the harbor, just 250 meters from this bunker. It has not yet docket. Thousands are waiting here on this side, the head end of the basin. They're all waiting to see whether it will dock on the right or the left side. I know where the gangplank will be lowered. Down below, at the bunker entrance, I have a motorcycle with a sidecar. I'll carry you down now, put you in the sidecar and take you to the proper place, see?"

"Yes," I said, "thank you."

When we got outside, it started to pour. The waiting throng scurried under cover. In the fog and rain the ship was a shadowy form in the middle of the harbor basin. It seemed gigantic to me. My sailor opened the throttle and, making a wide arc around the crowd, roared up to the left quayside. At the same time the heavy ship turned definitely toward us and that was the signal for thousands, heedless of the rain, to surge over to our side. At that moment, however, shrill whistles came from behind, followed by the cracks of shots. The crowd parted, terrified, and through the path thus formed an SS unit stormed forward toward the ship. They came up to our ground and formed a chain that cut off the rest of the quay. At the same time, the ship's gangplank was being lowered and medical orderlies were coming down carrying stretchers. Suddenly we were pushed from behind. Two orderlies had just laid me on a stretcher and carried me to óne side when an uncontrollable wave of human

beings swept the motorcycle and the foremost fifty or hundred people over the quay wall and the ship, at a depth of eight or ten meters, the unfortunate clung to each other in order to keep from plunging down themselves. Between the quay wall and the ship, at a depth of eight or ten meters, the unfortunate ones drowned like rats in the icy, oily water.

The SS forced order. I looked for my sailor, in order to thank him, but he had disappeared.

A loudspeaker from the ship announced that only the seriously wounded would be allowed on the ship. An SS officer and one of the ship's doctors stood at the bottom of the gangplank where orderlies opened up bandages on the spot, regardless of the rain. The doctors decided who was seriously wounded. At the ship's entrance there was another doctor or officer who assigned the beds. I was one of the first to be carried into the ship.

I had made it! I looked around. "General Steuben, 18,000 tons, formerly Hamburg-American Line, luxury cruiser," the orderly said. Although it had a coat of gray camouflage paint and was not marked as a hospital ship, it was equipped as such. I caught a glimpse of the drawing-rooms. They contained long rows of straw sacks for emergency beds. A few stairs, corridors, doors, then all was quiet. I was in my cabin.

It was a windowless inner cabin with two regular beds and an emergency bed. Orderlies washed me, cleaned out my wounds and bandaged them. I finally discovered that my second bullet had also left the body; but the resulting wound in the buttocks was so small that it had already healed and formed a crust. The present doctor also said that I had been very lucky, since the bullet had been deflected by the pelvic bone. It looked as though the shot had gone straight through the bone. He said it should all be healed in a few weeks. I shaved, was given a gown and was permitted to order all the food I wanted. It was like a dream. I immediately felt wonderful. One of my cabinmates was also satisfied, for he had no pain, though both legs were in a cast and he had a wound in his upper arm. The other occupant groaned and often screamed with pain. His leg was shattered; soon he had a hemorrhage. The doctor came and ordered him to the operating room. It was quiet again. There were only occasional noises from the outside, a few shots and some screaming that could be heard even in the cabin. What could be going on outside?

When the steward came, we had all kinds of questions.

"Where is the ship going?"

"To Swinemünde."

"Wonderful, that's farther than the Russians can walk. If something should go wrong, where's the exit?"

"Around the corner to the right, down the corridor, then right again. That's the emergency door to the outside."

"Life jackets?"

"Under your pillow. Description beside you on the wall."

"When do we start?"

"Nine o'clock, we hope."

"When do we get there?"

"Tomorrow morning."

"What's the news on the radio?"

"Not good, Lieutenant.—You'll feel better now."

I took a look at the life jacket and read the directions, knocked on the wooden commode, glanced at my watch; it was shortly before nine o'clock at night.

Now we felt the vibration of the propeller. From the distance, again the noise of shooting and a few calls. Then the steward returned and reported that we had just put off from shore. Goodbye, East Prussia, goodbye everybody. But at this final moment, joy was mixed with sadness as I thought of Ulli, Reichenbacher, my comrades, the refugees, the universal misery.

The turbines with their steady vibration finally lulled me to sleep. It was the first time in weeks that I slept without the tense feeling of imminent danger, responsibility, hunger, cold or despair. I was on the way home. My role as a soldier was finished, the future was more important now. The anti-aircraft guns on board and the convoy would protect us. I was in the seventh heaven.

A dull, heavy blow awakened me abruptly. I turned on the light and sat up. A ripping crunch shook the entire body of the ship. Alarmed, I looked at my neighbor. Outside there was shouting and running.

"What was that? A mine? Perhaps we've struck a rock?" The light stayed on and the turbines kept running. The shouting grew louder. Finally the steward came.

"A torpedo has hit us starboard. It could have been worse. No need to get excited."

There was no imminent danger. I looked at my service watch: 11:55. The steward had already disappeared. We tried to keep calm. We have no porthole, I said to myself, and thought of the emergency exit. I groped for my life jacket; but what are we to do—that one in his casts and I with my two wounds? Outside we heard a loudspeaker: "The commander speaking. Please keep calm. We've been hit by a torpedo. The hole has been sealed off by watertight bulkheads. There is no immediate danger. Everybody back to their places."

This calmed us somewhat and, since there were no further noises, I turned off the light and lay back on my pillows. After all, a heavy canoe like this one ought to be able to digest a torpedo.

Suddenly the ship listed to starboard. My heart stopped beating. Cups crashed to the floor, closet doors flew open. I turned the light back on. Deafening noise outside, clatter, rumbling and screaming. I was rolled out of bed and had to cling to the bedpost. The ship stayed on its side at a forty-five-degree angle; I was terrified that it would turn over again. The propellers stopped, but the light stayed on. I pulled myself upright, yanked my uniform jacket from the cupboard and fastened the life jacket around my chest. My bandages dropped off, my legs shook, but I was standing upright. I looked at my neighbor; he was about to draw a pair of trousers over his casts. "Don't bother with trousers, take the life jacket from the other bed and come on outside," I yelled as I dragged myself to the corridor.

The wounded were crawling along the corridor, others were climbing over them and dashing in the direction of the emergency exit. I managed to get as far as the side corridor where fifty men were pressing against a door that opened inward. We were on the listing side of the ship; people were piling up, the ones at the bottom gasping for help and unable to open the door. Out of here! I pulled myself by the handrail, back to the main staircase amidships. The steps were wide, but as a result of the sloping position of the ship, one could pull oneself up only by the handrail. An interlocked chain of soldiers was working its way upward, step by step. Others, coming from below, were climbing along the handrail itself, mercilessly stepping on the fingers of the crawling ones, so that some had to let go and the entire human snake slid back down the stairs. There was the crack of pistol shots, screaming, whimpering and weeping. With great difficulty I reached the door leading onto the open deck. I was on the top side, approximately amidships. As the icy wind hit my face and my unprotected body,the lights went out. A cry of horror and despair rang through the ship. Anyone still in the interior of the ship was lost, no doubt about it.

Soon my eyes became accustomed to the dark. I saw stars and moving clouds. The wide deck was looming up in front of me, obscuring my view of the sea. Above, on the railing, people were apparently trying to make up their minds whether or not to leap into the water; many were in nightclothes, few wore life jackets. Above me swung life boats full of women and children, but they could not be lowered into the water; the ship was listing so sharply that they would have hit the deck. Mothers and children who had become separated were screaming for each other. Sea chests and heavy iron parts became detached from the planks near the railing, skidded across the icy floors and crashed against the wounded who were coming from the interior and were dragging themselves along the cabin walls. I discovered a couple of rods with which I pulled myself upward along the windows, high enough so that finally nothing was above me. Clothed only in my uniform jacket, I felt chilled to the bone.

From here I was able to survey practically the entire ship. I was clinging to the outer wall of the pilot cabin. Because of the looming deck, however, I was still unable to see the water. The view from here was ghostly. I looked at my watch: twelve after midnight. My confidence in my survival was so great that I observed everything with the detachment of a reporter.

A long, dark cloud was moving across the moon; it was like the shadow of death. The ship was sinking toward the stern. Human voices had suddenly ceased. I looked forward. The bow had already disappeared in the swirling foam. In front of me, higher and higher, in gigantic masses, the black sea was coming toward me like a wall. I heard the churning of the water coming nearer. The spray shot higher and higher. Fifteen meters more. Then ten. Then five. My God. I let go of the rod, took a deep breath and was swept into the vortex of a giant wave. Simultaneously, another wave bore me upward. Somebody was clutching my back. I thrashed about wildly, sank, surfaced, freed myself, swallowed water, and then realized that my life jacket was carrying me. My pounding heart seemed near to bursting and I gasped for air. Suddenly I was tossed against a floating barrel. I felt as though I were losing consciousness, but then, for the first time, I felt the merciless cold of the water. The salt water made me vomit. I kicked my legs, in order to lift myself higher in the water; I was standing, rather than floating, in my life jacket. The waves were getting smaller and soon they were merely rolling me back and forth. I looked around and could see perhaps fifty meters. A great deal of wreckage was floating about, but there were only a few human beings. There was not a trace of the gigantic ship; silently, without explosion or fire, it had sunk in a matter of seconds. Cries of help became fewer and fiften minutes later it was deathly quiet. Sky, moving clouds with the moon coming through now and then, waves, sea.

I was completely numb below the waist, but the cold no longer bothered me much. I had not had time to think. Now, in the quiet of the night, my spirit returned. What are your chances? Good, I told myself. You have a life jacket; it will keep you afloat even if you should lose consciousness. Convoy planes are sure to come along soon. They must find me before I freeze to death. I looked at my service watch, the only thing I had left; it said 12:40. So it really was waterproof. An hour ago I was still sleeping peacefully. I was just thinking of the Russian subs that had caught us, when I saw a swaying black object before me. I was startled because it looked like a submarine tower. Then I realized it was an inflated raft and as it came nearer I saw three forms huddled together on it, back to back. I paddled closer and grabbed a mooring rope. I yelled at the figures, implored, howled, swore and cursed them. They did not stir. Perhaps they were dead and frozen stiff. I simply could not swing myself up on the raft alone. Nor could I hang on longer. The life was going out of my arm. I let go and tried to stay near the raft by paddling. But that, too, was impossible and slowly the strange craft floated away.

For a full hour I was utterly alone and only my watch with its illuminated dial kept me awake. I constantly moved my arms and rubbed them. My lips were too stiff to whistle or talk, so I started to sing. I sang until I was hoarse.

Then—wasn't that the sound of a motor? On each little wave crest I looked round about me. It was totally dark and windless. Suddenly a searchlight and the noise of ship turbines rose out of the dark. A ship was coming closer and closer. I was wide awake now and bellowed with all my might. It came so close that I saw it distinctly and heard voices on board. But no one heard me down there in the sea. And as quickly as it had approached, it disappeared. I couldn't believe it. The searchlight had once come quite close. They'll come back; they must. But another half hour went by before I heard them again. This time they did not come close, and soon that dream also evaporated.

I fell into a sort of stupor and simply listened; I no longer moved. Another half hour and my guardian spirit returned. At first I thought I was dreaming again; then it became obvious that someone was crying, "Hau ruck" and again "Hau ruck."* No doubt about it, a life boat was approaching. I yelled at the top of my lungs. I heard voices and someone saying, "Quiet, isn't that somebody calling?" Again I yelled and out of the darkness I saw a life boat swaying toward me. A woman's voice, "There I see him; I see somebody swimming." I fainted.

Hours later I woke up. My first feeling was that it was boiling hot. I found myself on a table with a towel over my hips. Someone was shouting, "Hurray, he's awake." And immediately five men started working on me, massaging me. I was feeling drunk, but before I knew it, another shot of cognac was being poured down my throat. "My dear Lazarus, you made it!" a bearded ruffian cried. I was sweating like mad. Then I listened to their story.

I had lain in the life boat another hour until it was finally picked up by a mine-sweeper. It had contained mostly women, and only three such boats had been found. Very few survivors who were floating about alone had been saved. The women had rowed simply to keep warm, but since they could not see anything in the dark, they had constantly rowed in a circle near the scene of the disaster. The mine sweeper had had orders to keep searching the waters until dawn.

The present situation turned out to be unfortunate for us. There was not enough fuel to take us to Swinemünde; hence we would have to dock in Kollberg, in Pomerania. The Russians were already in Stettin and Pomerania was a new pocket surrounded by Russians.

*Stroke — feather, stroke — feather.

In a few hours I had recovered wonderfully and I was certain that, except for my hands and feet, I had suffered no ill effects from my icy swim. The salt water may have even been beneficial to my wounds. However, my hands and feet remained numb and this disturbed me. My uniform jacket, the only article of clothing I possessed, was dry. I was placed on a stretcher and, when we docked in Kollberg, I was wrapped in a blanket and taken off the boat. We were the last of the search vessels and convoys, the last survivors. After we had been counted, an army captain told me, "There were 3000 seriously wounded on board the 'General Steuben.' At the last minute, 500 women and children were allowed to go aboard. The crew numbered 500, including the anti-aircraft gun crew, the hospital crew and eighty Red Cross nurses. We counted 150 saved from a total of 4000, unless there were some rescued by other boats that we do not know of. And no names are known to us!"

I asked whether the mine sweeper would refuel and take us farther. "How can you ask? We haven't a drop of fuel. The boat has to remain here and you'll be put in the hospital."

Women and children were now crowding up to us and giving us homemade cakes and sweets. They were all weeping. Kollberg had heard of the catastrophe and many had come to the harbor to greet the survivors. It was well meant, but what a sad welcome!

A truck took us to a former girls' school that had been converted into a field hospital. When we were admitted, I realized that we represented nothing special; the tragedy that was pressing in at these doors was so overwhelming that the individual and his experiences did not count. I was happy to be assigned a bed with a straw sack and I heaved a big sigh as I sank into the fresh sheets.

It was an emergency hospital, hastily equipped, and everything was lacking. Even the bandages were made of paper. The food was inedible. Doctors and nurses worked to the point of exhaustion. I was in the third story, in a former teachers' room. My roommates, both of them captains, spoke scarcely a word. One of them had a dreadful abdominal injury; instead of a testicle, he had a gaping hole from which rubber tubes were suspended. He was pale and drawn. At night I heard him weep softly. The other man had a small radio beside his bed. He asked for quiet whenever news came; it came constantly and was always devastating. We were caught in the Pomeranian ring. All the available ships that had fuel were ordered to the Baltic states and to East Prussia, to rescue the people there. Kollberg itself was preparing feverishly for a siege. Russian tank spearheads were coming nearer and the circle was closing around us. Once, I asked the doctor pointblank what his plans were. He said he was in touch with the harbor and the airfield, but there simply wasn't any possibility of our being transported. We would have to be realistic and prepare to face captivity. Since we had no reserves whatever, we were completely at the mercy of the Russians.

"Mercy of the Russians—don't make me laugh!" one of my roommates snickered.

"It's too late to laugh," whispered the other one.

The doctor left.

The days crept by, and our helpless condition was demoralizing. On February 16th I wrote a letter home. It actually reached my mother; the German army postal service performed miracles.—The sound of a Junker 52, a big, old hospital plane was heard every day around noon. Out of a clear sky, without any particular plan, I decided to do something unusual. I got up, leaned on two crutches and hobbled on the outside of my bandaged feet into the corridor. I opened the door of the orderly room. The sergeant must have thought he was seeing a ghost; he leapt up and wanted to help me.

"I should like to ask a favor of you," I said. "I have a sweetheart here in Kollberg whom I'd like to call up. I have her number. Could I be alone for a few minutes?"

"Why, of course, Lieutenant, that's perfectly all right," said the sergeant, pointed to the telephone and closed the door behind him.

On the wall above the desk hung a list of names and telephone numbers. I immediately found what I was looking for—the airport number. With a pencil between my thumb and my bandaged fist I dialed a number. A woman's voice answered with a code of designation. I asked for the commander. "Air station or Captain Mueller, air field?"

"Mueller," I replied gruffly, my heart beating wildly.

"Mueller," a weary voice came over the wire.

"Captain Mueller, my name is Heck, Lieutenant Heck. I am lying here in the emergency hospital in the Kollberg girls' school. I am one of the survivors of the 'Steuben' disaster which you may have heard about. I'm a young, knocked-up infantry lieutenant and I'm asking you simply man to man to give me a chance. Every day I hear planes flying over; I could be transported sitting up. I know my request is unusual and against all rules. Do you have anything to say to me, Captain?"

For a few seconds I heard him breathing. Then he said, "Come on out here; we have a bed for you in our Red Cross station. Whether you're captured here or in Kollberg won't matter. At least you'll have better food here. I can't have you called for; we haven't a drop of gasoline. If you manage to get here, you might have a chance in a thousand."

He hung up. My knees were buckling and I sat down. The sergeant looked in.

"Everything in order?" he asked.

"And how! She's getting everything ready for me and is expecting me!"

"Boy, oh boy, the bachelors have it all over us," he laughed.

"What I need, but quickly, are a shirt, trousers, galoshes that'll fit over my bandages, a coat, cap and two crutches."

"I'll see what can be done, Lieutenant."

An hour later he turned up in my room. The clothing was old and worn, but that, of course, did not bother me.

"What are your plans?" the others asked. I repeated my sweetheart story. Even the doctor seemed to believe it and finally gave me permission to leave the hospital, provided I came back frequently, especially if Kollberg were occupied and surrendered. Under the Red Cross, he said, there might be more hope than a wounded person on his own could expect.

After lunch I set out. I was unable to get crutches because they would all be needed if the hospital should be captured; instead, I had two skylight rods that one of the orderlies had detached for me; they looked like thin walking sticks. Huge guard boots fitted over my bandages and, thus equipped, I hobbled out into the snow.

I must have looked quite impossible, for passers-by stood still and shook their heads; a few asked whether they could help me. It was just a step to the main street where I simply sat down on the curb and hailed passing vehicles. A farmer stopped and helped me up onto his horsecart. He had been loading pressed straw for the defense trenches on the outskirts of the city. I told him I had to get to the airport and he agreed to take me. At the edge of the city, women, children, and old men were engaged in digging tank traps. The airport was a few kilometers outside the city; and when we finally drew up in front of it, I felt as though we had come from another planet.

Here everything was in model, peacetime order. All during these years, the war had been but a casual visitor here, when fighter planes took off and returned with their reports—or when they failed to return. At the moment, it was an air base without aircraft, since there was no fuel. And so the pilots, well-groomed and rested were probably going to the movies with chic air-force aides and coming back late at night, no doubt whistling; "The end of a perfect day." What's that about the war moving closer? Well, then let's practice a bit of recoilless grenade discharging. That is what they were doing in one corner of the field and from all appearances, they seemed to be enjoying themselves. Who said Ivan is coming here? Nonsense! Even if he does, old Herrmann will get us out of here.—That was the general impression I had as we drove across the airfield. I was stared at like a man from Mars. We inquired our way through to Captain Mueller. A few men followed and wanted to know whether I had come directly from the front. Captain Mueller had me carried to the Red Cross station, and for a few minutes I was alone with him in a small vestibule.

"Here you'll at least have good food and a decent bed. Let me outline the situation here: We have no fuel for our planes and aren't getting any more. A single tank is at our disposal for the one Ju52 that makes a daily flight from Berlin to Heiligenbeil, to take on the wounded and the last important Party men. On its return flight it has to stop here for refueling. But soon business will be over with Heiligenbeil. Since yesterday there has been fighting at the airport there. That would be the end with East Prussia as far as we are concerned. This single Ju is filled to the brim, as you can imagine. The chance I mentioned to you on the phone would come if somebody should die on the flight from East Prussia; then you could take his place."

Holy smoke, what a chance, I thought. I thanked him briefly told him my story which seemed to impress him, and asked him to keep me posted. Thereupon, I was assigned a bed and fell into it exhausted.

The room had five beds, two of which were occupied. One man had a racking cough; the other, gonorrhea. The doctor, a Lett, spoke very broken German and looked handsome in his air-force uniform. I couldn't help but marvel at everything.

My first night at the airfield was filled with nightmares. I woke up, bathed in sweat, and could not go back to sleep, worrying about who would get here first: Ivan or my plane.

The next day at noon I heard the plane. I was already dressed and when the Ju landed, an orderly ran over for me, in order to size up the situation. He soon returned: no luck, not a chance. A half hour later, the plane took off.

The next night brought dense fog and, on the radio, a report of heavy fighting in the Heiligenbeil area where my last chance was supposed to be coming from. There was no plane all day. What had happened? Had Heiligenbeil capitulated? Nobody seemed to know, or else they were not saying.

Another day, more fog. Toward noon it cleared and at two o'clock a Ju came roaring in. I was waiting in my room, on needles and pins; yes, waiting for someone to die and bequeath me his place on the plane—my last chance. The door opened and in came two beat-up looking front officers, partly supported by orderlies. They were plastered with bandages, slings and dirt, and it was difficult to make out their rank. One of them was apparently a captain with a knight's cross; the other wore a long leather coat and his bandaged arm covered all military insignia. They had evidently come with the plane. A great fuss was being made about them, cognac and sandwiches were brought. Then they were left alone for a while and sat there with heads bowed, staring into space.

"Do you have any room left on the plane? I must get on. It's my last hope." These were my first words since their arrival.

They both looked at me for the first time. Then the one in the leather coat said, "What's the matter with you?"

The more I told them, the more interested they seemed to become. Moreover, it turned out that we had fought as neighbors in East Prussia. They held a whispered consultation, whereupon one of them said, "All right, marathon swimmer, Stick close to us from now on. You'll come with us, I'll see to it."

"My name is Lieutenant Heck."

"Cavalry Captain Meier, and I'm Colonel von Breda, Commander Tank Division Grossdeutschland."

As he spoke, the arm sling had shifted and I saw on his collar his knight's cross with swords and diamonds, one of the highest, most impressive decorations of the war. Hope and confidence filled me; I knew that the word of such a man was law.

Twenty minutes later we were loaded onto a hand-drawn canvas cart and rolled to the plane. I had modestly taken a seat between the two and nobody objected. There stood the big Ju52 in drizzle and light fog, old and solid, clumsy yet reassuring. A couple of mechanics were working on the motors. Below the entrance stood a few men who were about to enter when the Captian was lifted in. From above I heard scolding and cries of pain. The pilot came up to me and was about to speak when the Colonel called to him, "How many more can get on?"

Angry curses were the spontaneous reply; the pilot turned to the Colonel, "We discussed the problem in Heligenbeil, Colonel; we can't go through it all once more. I am responsible for the plane. We can't take on any more than we came with." He looked at me. All this time an air force lieutenant with a brief case, perfect creases in his trousers and clean boots had been standing next to the Colonel.

"Good, in that case I suggest that we take this young wounded lieutenant. You"—he looked straight at the air force lieutenant who was growing pale—"will stay here. You are well and can take care of yourself. I can't refuse your wounded comrade."

"Colonel, I am flying on an urgent mission to the main headquarters of the Führer. I have been authorized to use this plane."

"You can entrust me with your papers. I am speaking to the Führer myself, and shall explain the situation to your superiors."

"No, I am answerable with my life for the documents."

"Very well, I can't force you. Help this lieutenant up!" the Colonel said sharply, pointed to me and held out his hand in farewell to the other.

The Colonel was the last to squeeze through the door. The motors started revving up. I looked out through the little window. The young lieutenant was being swallowed up by rain and fog. The plane bumped along, then touched off and, for the first time in my life, I was flying. I was feeling uncomfortable, and not because I was flying. Someone next to me was saying that the lieutenant need not wait for any more planes; it was all over in Heiligenbeil and this was undoubtedly the last plane to make it.

The flight was terrible. Everywhere the wounded, squeezed together, were groaning. I could not move. The air was scarcely endurable. We flew very low. Enemy formations were said to be approaching Berlin. We leaped over woods and lakes. Once somebody said, "This is the Oder. The front is already here." And the radio was still talking about forthcoming miracle weapons and fresh divisions. When, for God's sake, with the Russians on their way to Berlin!

Ah, Berlin. We were dropping down toward the sea of houses. We've made it! As we were being lifted out, the air-raid siren sounded. Directly behind us a rocket airplane was landing on runners like skis. A monstrous ray of fire was coming out the end of it and the pilot seemed to be lying on his belly as he was lowered out. We were immediately transported to a surface bunker where we were divided up. I scarcely had an opportunity to thank Colonel von Breda. A doctor explained to us that Berlin was under constant heavy air attacks, that the hospitals were overcrowded and only the most serious cases could remain here. He requested us to leave Berlin immediately; a train for Bavaria was waiting.

In ambulances we were driven to the Anhalter Station, and Red Cross nurses helped us into the train. I got a seat in a compartment with refugees from Dresden. Here I learned of the catastrophic attacks by American and English fliers on this city which had hitherto been spared. It must have been an incredible night that reduced Dresden to rubble and ashes. More people were said to have died in that one night than in any single military action of the war. These people in the train were despairing, desolate, hungry, but not prepared to deliver up the Germans to Russia. The general opinion was that the Amis would call a halt to the Russians and that the other conceivable solution would be for us, together with America and England, to drive Russia out of our country.

"But don't you see that the Allies are destroying our cities and bombing the civilians!"

"Oh, yes, those are the Jews. Wait and see; they'll shake off the Jews one day too."

"Unconditional surrender. Do you know what that means? It means they will castrate the German men, rape our women and starve us all out. That Jew Morgenthau has planned it all."

Thus the conversation went on.

I was ordered to Bad Mergentheim. I had to change trains once; and finally, after a long night, I reached the dreamy, peaceful-looking spa of Mergentheim. I was helped out of the train and swayed on my strange crutches over to the postoffice. The window had just opened. I asked whether they could connect me by phone with Weinheim. "Oh, that would have to go by way of Mannheim and there all the trunk lines are down."

"Well, try anyway," I insisted and made myself comfortable on the bench. After a few minutes the official cried, "Weinheim! why I can't believe it."

"Mother!" My voice choked. She was incredulous, for she had not yet received my last letter and thought I was somewhere in Poland. She promised to visit me within the next few days.

I inquired about military hospitals and learned of a small one at St. Rochus Convent. When I telephoned there and described my situation, I was called for in a horse and buggy. Eighty beds, a chicken farm, and apiary, Catholic nuns—I actually felt close to heaven; and when, after a sumptuous breakfast, a bath and a cigarette, I ventured a nap, I did not wake up until late afternoon. I could not have been more fortunate. The rest, the treatment, the food, the garden, the early spring—I was restored to life. My wounds and frostbite were healing rapidly. Soon I could walk without a stick, though still somewhat bent.

A week later Mother succeeded in hitch-hiking to Bad Mergentheim to visit me. On my first walk with her on my arm, through the park of the spa, I was in civilian clothing and felt on top of the world. Mother reported that Weinheim, like nearby Heidelberg, had not yet suffered bomb damage, that the Americans were at the Rhine, near Mannheim, a half-hour's ride from Weinheim. She believed and hoped that it could not last much longer, that since there were no troops in Weinheim, no fighting was expected there. She had had news of Hans who had managed to get out of the east and was now in Copenhagen. Thank God, now I no longer doubted my family's ultimate survival. We tried to talk about the future, but it was impossible; from now on every day of the war would make our prospects more hopeless.

A few days after Mother's departure the order reached us that every available bed had to be vacated at once for a new shipment of wounded from the western front. The doctor decided that I could be treated at home. Since no more trains were going west, I, too, tried hitch-hiking. In the Neckar Valley, not far from Heidelberg, a low-flying plane came within a hair of strafing us. At the last moment, the driver yanked the car into an underpass just as the sheaves of fire crashed into the street.

At home there was great rejoicing. Mother and my grandparents were living in a garret in a one-family house. The owner was finally compelled to take refugees, which made the atmosphere rather strained when at night, thanks to air alarms, they were obliged to meet in the cellar. The Americans were moving closer and were hourly expected in Weinheim. Thank God, I still had a uniform. Despite the general situation, I was anxious at least to look like a lieutenant.

First of all, I reported to the commanding officer of the town. To my amazement, the old man said: "What luck! Take over my job for half a day; I have to see how my family is getting along." And with that he was gone. A non-commissioned officer with a wooden leg was sitting in the office; he spoke of a quiet job, no excitement, no troops, no defense. "If only the bombs don't start raining down on us the last minute!" That seemed to be the general attitude. A local industrialist, Richard Freudenberg, stuck his head into the door, in order to be assured once more that not a soul here was thinking of defense. In the evening the "commander" returned, obviously disappointed that the Amis were not yet here.

I visited an uncle who had suddenly hired a Ukrainian servant girl and was treating her with extreme friendliness, while my aunt kept repeating to me that the girl had been in a concentration camp. Bed sheets were kept in readiness as flags; Party literature, uniforms and Party insignia were buried. All these were preparations for "afterwards."

When I got home there was another air alarm. In the cellar, I made the acquaintance of the landlord who introduced me to his son, an uncomfortable looking non-commissioned officer who, without waiting for the question I had no intention of asking, blurted out something about just passing through on a two-day leave.

"Very good," I said. But four hours later, during the next alarm, the landlord said to me, "Lieutenant, what do you intend to do when the Amis come? My son knows what he must do; he is on his way to the front." His voice rose slightly as he spoke.

"Good for you," I remarked calmly.

"Don't worry about me."

His remark had sufficed; I realized I could not stay here. The question for me was: uniform or civilian clothes; if I am in uniform, I am endangering the others in the house and will be automatically captured. If I am in civilian clothes, the Amis will soon find out that I am a lieutenant and might regard me as a spy. However, if German troops or even SS troops in a last-minute counter-offensive should find me in civilian clothes, I could be accused of being a deserter or a traitor. I therefore decided the next morning to go a block farther to an emergency hospital and there surrender to the Amis.

Early in the morning I heard shooting; two *Landsers* ran through the street. At eight o'clock the sirens sounded. I was standing in the doorway of the hospital. From the intersection at Mother's house I heard tank chains rattling and saw a heavy Ami tank appear. At the same time, a vintner with a handcart, carrying a small white flag, was coming down the street. On the cart was a coffin. The vintner was headed directly for the intersection where the tank had just appeared. He went doggedly on, ignoring the tank. The turret hatch opened and an astonished Ami shook his head, called out something to the man, but he shuffled on in the direction of the graveyard.

A group of infantrymen came crawling along the walls of the houses. When they saw me, they came cautiously up to me. I raised my arms, stepped out into the street and pointed to the large Red Cross flag above me. I had finally met up with the Americans. It was March 18, 1945. I was a prisoner of the U.S. Army, a POW, a Kraut.

I was the only officer in the hospital; the doctors had disappeared. With my halting school English I assured the Amis that we had no weapons; we were approximately fifty wounded men, a few nurses and helpers. Four Amis made a brief inspection, whereupon two guards remained behind at the doors of the building, and we were left alone.

March 18, 1945. It was a strange feeling. Somehow, we had hoped until the last that the decisive blow would come which would leave Germany, if not victorious, at least not totally vanquished. But now that we were invaded and captured, the oppressive uncertainty of the defeated gave way to utter indifference. All we could think was: let's hope our troops don't attempt a counter-offensive; let's hope one of those miracle weapons does'nt crash down on our own heads; let's hope the war will end soon now; let's hope the Amis will stop the Russians.

Two hours after the occupation, our two doctors had reappeared in the emergency hospital. Then came an American doctor and wanted to know what we needed in the way of medicines and food. The head doctor ordered the interpreter to say that we would not accept American help, which was, of course, stupid pride. Thank God, the Ami did not understand and the order was not even translated. Four hours later, the first Ami trucks rolled into the courtyard, filled with medicines, white bread, coffee, chocolate, cigarettes and all kinds of other things. The head doctor was the first to try a cigarette and announced, "Slight opium content." Nevertheless, he helped himself to a pack.

Our spirits were rising. We were permitted to talk to friends and family through the open windows. We were always treated with civility, almost friendliness; the first combat troops paid little attention to the anti-fraternization law prohibiting Americans to speak to Germans. Negro soldiers, especially, were soon enjoying great popularity because they took pity on hungry children and distributed chocolate. Rumor had it that from here we would be sent home.

On my birthday, April 9, Mother was permitted to visit me and bring me a birthday cake. She was in despair and described how the Amis had confiscated our few rooms and how she had, with great difficulty, rescued only a few belongings and found shelter with friends.

Incidentally, on the second day of my captivity, I saw the landlord's son, who had presumably heroically gone to the front, parading down the street in civilian clothes. All male civilians were requested to report daily to the authorities of the occupation forces at the town hall. Mother told me that on one such trip the young man had not returned. The Amis had simply loaded him on a truck and taken him to France to a POW camp. Later, we learned that he was handed over to the French who needed workers in their mines. It was two years before the poor devil, slightly disillusioned no doubt, showed up once more in Weinheim.

Toward the middle of April there was a count taken of the wounded who were halfway restored to health. One of my wounds was still open; I was still walking with a stick and had considerable pain. However, the head doctor could not stand me, and so I was among those who were discharged. Discharged into captivity. Trucks rolled into the courtyard and before we knew it or could notify our families, we roared off. Ten kilometers beyond, we were driven out on a field. The Amis had us lined up, divested us of our wrist watches, rings and fountain pens, all of whch they threw into a carton, and loaded us onto trucks again. Our captivity had now begun in earnest and the war was not yet over.

The dusty journey took us in the direction of the Rhine, across an American pontoon brige. We were deposited in a dreadful transient prisoner camp. At night the field was brightly illuminated and from nearby Worms we heard the alarm sirens. All we needed now was to be bombed by our own fliers! The thirsty ones fought at the few water faucets. It was incredibly depressing. German volunteers with armbands were helping the Amis. God knows what sort of men they were; they shouted at the German officers, spat on them, kicked them and boxed their ears. Finally, we were loaded into open freight cars, and once more the station signs changed from German—this time into French. The intermediate stations in Vauve and Epinal are worth mentioning only because there we were joined by a new group of *Landsers* who seemed to have come from another planet. They were prisoners of the last Runstead offensive, or, as the Amis said, 'the Battle of the Bulge. They were full of pep, they were convinced of ultimate victory, spoke constantly of treason and of having been stabbed in the back. They kept devising plans of escape and wanted to break through to some Atlantic fortifications that were still being held by German troops. There followed the first unfriendly arguments. But when the train started up again, discussion languished in the noise of the cattle cars. Moreover, the rumor that a German prisoner transport was on its way had preceded us, so that at town railroad crossings French heroes threw buckets of rotten eggs, manure and sticks into our open cars. An old officer who for the third day had been trying to explain to the doctor that he was a diabetic and needed insulin fell into one coma after another, as he held in his hand the box containing the needle. We reached the vicinity of Cherbourg.

It was astonishing what the Amis had captured and dragged here to Cherbourg. There were Hitler youths and eighty-year-old-prisoners of the cavalry corps, railroad stationmasters, postal officers, air-raid wardens, Party peasants and policy officers, SS men and *Landsers*, generals, admirals and foresters. It was a motley crowd, some of them disciplined and poised, in parade uniforms, others ragged, beaten, and despairing, divested of their uniforms and camouflaged in Bavarian jackets, carrying leather satchels or bread bags.

The guards in the Cherbourg camp were Poles in Ami uniforms dyed dark blue. Their behavior toward us was sometimes annoying even to the Americans. And yet, how could G.I. Kilroy of Matawan, N.J. know what had happened in Lodjz, Poland! Some of the Amis apparently were better informed.

"Special Lt. Rosenbaum," the small sign read on the desk of the barracks through which everyone was obliged to pass. Rosenbaum's job was to put us through the red tape and divide us up into different camps. First we were examined for SS tattooing under our right arms— something I had not known about until then. It was the blood-type sign with which every Waffen SS man was marked. Then we were introduced to our first questionnaires which were probably meant to find out whether we were to be classed as Nazis. Some of the questions were so childish that we laughed at them. Rosenbaum yelled at us in German and called us names. He wanted to know how many Jews each of us had on his conscience. It was hard for us to keep a straight face; we were tempted to spit on his perfumed hair. When he asked whether we felt ourselves to be Nazis, many answered yes, just to annoy him. He searched through long lists of names and read our papers with extreme care. Then he said something about six million gassed Jews. We looked at him pityingly. One of the men said, "Weren't there sixty million? Or maybe 600 million? I think 600 million volunteers!" Rosenbaum shouted at him with tears in his eyes and said that one day, "when you learn the truth which you refuse to face, your eyes too will fill with tears."

Everybody was given a blanket and off we went into the fields to which we were individually assigned. Captivity is degrading and inhuman, even when the treatment complies with the Geneva Convention. However, like so many other things, it must be experienced at least once. We were 1000 men in a camp on a level field enclosed with barbed wire. Our quarters were large tents which contained nothing. A camp of this kind was called a "cage." There were vast numbers of cages, so many that they could not be surveyed. It was said that this was an officer's camp with 40,000 German officers. We were permitted to leave our cage only on Sundays to go to church. Everybody went, of course, just for the sake of a change. The service was held in a large assembly tent, and afterwards we were allowed to go in groups to the football field. Now and then we could also go to the shower barracks for a bath and a medical check-up. To the left of us was a cage for generals. Forty or more generals walked up and down, some proudly, others utterly unkempt with long beards. It was a sad spectacle to see a German general stoop down to pick up a discarded Ami cigarette. To our right there was a special cage where Germans as well as Amis were serving out special punishments, for theft, brawls and so forth. These cages were equipped with wide corrugated tin barrels, open at the top and about eight feet high. By means of ladders the culprits were lowered into these barrels. They were given a blanket at night and daily rations of bread and water. Across the top of the barrels were placed planks for the guards who walked from barrel to barrel and looked down on the solitary victims broiling in the hot sun. Every day a doctor came by to inspect the men, and after eight days, as a rule, they had to be hauled out.

In our cage we seldom saw guards, since we were surrounded by other cages, but it was rumored that the guards were again Poles. We were able to see a high watch tower on which was mounted a huge loudspeaker. During the day and far into the night only one record was played, a coca cola commercial. Some wizard of a psychologist must have thought that up, to drive us insane. On the football field we rarely played, we were too busy meeting friends and acquaintances. A regular visitor was Colonel Rudel, Germany's most successful combat flier who, for his improbable tank shots on the eastern front, received the highest decoration of the war: the gold oak leaf on the knight's cross with swords and diamonds. The Amis took it away from him, as they did his artificial leg. I was told the Amis were afraid he might escape; I never had occasion to talk with him.

From the very first day the situation in our cage was rather dismal. The food rations were so ridiculously small that even the crumbs were carefully weighed on the home-made scales. We were constantly hungry and slowly we began to believe the rumor that the Amis were preparing us for the sub-standard existence which they felt the Germans deserved. The older men seemed to suffer more from hunger, and soon some of them collapsed and were taken away. However, the situation did not improve. True, the food was excellent, but a slice and a half of the best white bread per day or three tablespoons of creamed corn for dinner are scarcely enough. There was even a little tobacco which I exchanged for bread. Others started smoking discarded tea leaves and coffee grounds collected from the kitchen refuse, which soon resulted in threatened blindness.

Since we were officers, we were not permitted to work; and, condemned to idleness, we sat around in the summer heat like Indians. The only officer who was never seen without his immaculate uniform, including gloves, was Major von Glasenapp, a true nobleman who could sit all day on a box beside his tent with a salvaged French dictionary which he was systematically and quite literally learning by heart. When I left he had memorized as far as "Q." While I certainly did not wish him prolonged captivity, I felt it would be a pity if his sudden release would result in an everlasting gap from Q to Z in his French vocabulaary. He would presumably never have time to make it up later on, since immediately upon his release, he was planning to resume a top position in the rubber industry, which he had relinquished in order to become a reserve.

For entertainment and to give us something positive to do, we arranged evening lectures. Everyone in the tent had to give a talk on his profession or on some subject of general interest. If he was good, he gave his lecture for anyone in the camp who wanted to hear him. We had experts in all fields, and the talks were very instructive. The most interesting to me were the lectures on the stars given by an astronomy professor who talked in detail about constellations, formations, distances and our solar system. This meant a great deal to me, for day after day, week after week and month after month we lived on a small area under the open sky, a sky that represented the only certain, true and stable element and that led straight to God...

Religion was something new to most of us, and in every cage there were groups sitting together talking about it. All kinds of sects were formed; religious and philosophical problems were examined and discussed. It was a unique opportunity for evangelists and proselytizers.

Uncertainty about the future depressed us all. Those who had lost their homes in the east, who knew nothing about their families and who realized, from radio reports, that they would never be able to go back, suffered the most acutely. Then there were those whose homes and families were now in Russian-occupied zones and who were aware that the Russians would never give back any territory. The rest of us were West Germans whose homes had suffered the most from bomb destruction. Hence, in spite of all spiritual concerns, we were beginning to take an interest in everyday material matters as well: in the question of how to make beet sugar for home consumption or how to ferment home-grown tobacco.

Thus, life went on in the camp and the war was still not over. We were kept informed of the general situation by means of a system which had been organized from the very beginning. A camp eldest was elected who was also our spokesman with the Amis. Every morning we fell in line and were counted. Thereafter the sick were led to the medical barracks. The eldest then read the German military report for the day, which was followed by a translation of the official American report. After we had heard both reports, we were dismissed and returned to our tents where discussions began.

April 24th was Hitler's birthday. When we lined up on that morning, we were already wondering whether this day, always a special one in the Third Reich, would even be mentioned. The German military report noted it, but nothing happened and we were requested to return to our tents. There the commotion started. A few voices were raised in angry protest that the Führer was not being honored on his birthday. More and more voices joined in, demanding some sort of gesture. Then the anti-Hitlerites came to life and shouted down the others.

The Amis were quite puzzled about all this. They tried to explain to the camp eldest that they did not permit discussions of this kind, but meanwhile hand-to-hand fighting had broken out. Officers of all ranks and merits called each other traitors. The Amis had difficulty forcing us back into our tents where the shouting continued. It turned out that we had in our midst the unfortunate captain of the Remagen Rhine bridge, who had failed to blow up the bridge at the last moment, either because he had forgotten or because he was too cowardly or had had no time. He had thereupon been sentenced to death in absentia, and here he was. He was quite harmless, no traitor, no spy, no treacherous underground man, no cowardly bundle of nerves. He was completely normal, a typical family man in uniform. His story was so non-heroic that I've even forgotten it. What he now had to fear was the fury of his countrymen who would have preferred to pass judgment on him themselves. Yet these were anything but Party men; here the Party would not have had a leg to stand on. These were incorrigible, hard-bitten, daring types, most of them from the Ardennes group, who simply had not seen the light, who equated Hitler with honor, and Germany with Hitler. Then there were the others, the resisters, the superior officers who knew better, who had taken part in the unsuccessful Putsch against Hitler. They were acquainted with most of the facts and recounted details that made one's hair stand on end. There were still others, such as my tentmate Hilmar Feher, who was not a resister but who saw the situation for what it was and who had succeeded in freeing himself from the myth. He talked back excitedly and when he talked it was also in the name of Germany, a Germany which was now ashamed of Hitler. These political debates went on for days.

Then came the news of Hitler's death. The *Wehrmacht* report spoke of the death of a hero fighting at the head of his men for what was left of Berlin. The American report had not yet come out. After reading aloud the German report, the eldest said, "I ask each of you in this situation to observe with me two minutes of silence and to think of the man who became our destiny. His death releases you from your oath."

It was quiet for five seconds. Then, here and there, arms were raised in the German salute to honor Hitler. An officer cried, "Let us bow our heads and honor our fallen Führer with the German salute!"

"Shut up, snot nose, you don't know what you're saying!"

Again the men were shouting at each other. When they returned to their tents, many were shaking their heads and some were deeply moved; all were doubtless sore at heart.

During the next few days, various sections of the German army capitulated; the war was over. Russians and Americans met in Berlin. We had lost. We were beaten. If we believed that at least our honor had been saved, we would soon be informed otherwise. Slowly but surely, the details about the Jews and the exterminations filtered through. We looked at each other suspiciously. Everything that had seemed to us young men sacred and idealistic came crashing down in one dreadful revelation. We thought we had been asked to believe in lofty humanity as expressed in decency, candor, bravery, high-mindedness and sacrifice, but it turned out that we were meant to believe in the *Herrenmensch*, an individual with self-imposed authority to enslave or even to exterminate those who did not exemplify this concept. It was no use assuring ourselves that we had not known. The ideal itself, its creators and heralds, were inhuman. Germany followed them with open eyes, yet blindly, and upon us, the survivors, the finger of accusation was pointed. Hunger was coupled with despair. What could we expect of the future after this? The war was over; why wouldn't they just let us go home?

The summer heat set in. There was no mail, no news from home. Endless rumors circulated. Sunburned, starved and emaciated, we suffered on. Nor were we cheered by the news of the atom bomb.

"The work of the Jews," some of the men said.

"They would have tossed the thing at us if they'd had it earlier. Now the Jews are boasting about their strongest weapon which we really should have had."

"It's all a betrayal," others said.

"It was our own Göttingen invention. We have the scientists who thought the thing out; it was stolen and sold."

No one believed that the war could possibly be over for the Americans; we knew that Russia had to be driven out of Europe as soon as possibile. The Amis with their bomb now had the means of doing this. But nothing happened. We heard about "Papa Stalin" as though he were a humane statesman who stroked the heads of little children and wouldn't hurt a fly.

Finally, in September, discharges began. First came the old men over sixty, then those who had their families in the Russia zone of occupation. Suddenly all those disappeared who had never been in the army. After that, we were taken alphabetically, the U's through Z's. Next, those under twenty and the A's to H's. It was a trial of nerves. Finally, my turn came. We shouldered our self-made tin bowls and plates, took leave of our comrades and found ourselves in open box cars without food, on the journey through France. Once again, garbage and stones rained down on us from bridges. If the train stopped in an open field, many climbed down and dug turnips out of the fields. Our guards were indifferent.

After two days we reached Heilbronn in southern Germany. There we were given our discharge papers. It was the 18th of September. I hitchhiked through the beautiful Neckar Valley to Heidelberg. I had heard that at home there was no salt, so I stopped at a salt pit and, in view of my appearance, was permitted a whole bag full. However, when I saw hundreds of housewives waiting in line at the entrance to the pit and realized that I should be unable to carry my heavy sack, I gave away half of it and marched off with the rest in a paper bag over my shoulder, smiling to myself when I realized that this was all I was bringing back from the war.

When Mother saw me, she almost fainted with fright and joy. I was a mere skeleton and brown as a mulatto.

"What in the world are you carrying in that bag?"

"Salt, Mother enough for two years."

"Salt! That's the one thing we really don't need; we can buy plenty of it."

We screamed with laughter, and Hans joined us, He had come home a few weeks before from Denmark where he had been released from British captivity. My grandparents, who had also fled here from the approaching Russians, made our family large, but happy. We were all together again. We really had survived. That was all that mattered.

Here we were, city people, in this dreamy little village of Weinheim. On the black market, for vast sums of money, we bought coffee, flour and ham. From somewhere we even managed to get a bottle of wine. On the radio, one Gaston Ullman, commentator, spoke of the Nuremberg war criminals trial. We listened with mixed feelings.

The next day, an American came into the house, looked at our two rooms, counted all the furniture and announced that in two hours we would have to vacate the rooms, that an American lieutenant would be moving in. He warned us not to remove any furniture. Then he took the center pillow of one sofa we had saved, tossed it into his jeep and roared off singing. This was the eighth time that Mother had had to give up the place she was living in, and each time we lost more of the belongings that had been rescued from our house in Cologne. Weinheim's arch-Communist who had been assigned to the housing office by the Amis got us into the private house of a former Party member. We hastily removed our furniture and replaced it with junk that we had discovered in the attic. Then we went to the town hall to collect our food stamps. The feeling of walking about an undamaged town as a free citizen in civilian clothes was indescribably satisfying. What matter that the shop windows were empty, that one's suit no longer fit! Girls' eyes looked at you; life was coming back. Peace had broken out.

There were five problems still unsolved: food, housing, work, politics and the future, and how to enjoy life under these circumstances. At the moment, there was chaos. Since West Germany, with its overpopulation, could not feed itself, we depended on imports. With our industry

Klaus at Christmas, 1945-46

Klaus, Hans, and Mother, 1945-46.

shattered, we were unable to produce anything, nor did we have the raw materials. Our money was worthless; hence, no one was willing to trade with us. The system of ration cards was an inadequate attempt fairly to distribute the little we had. It did not provide enough to live on. As a result, everyone who could walk set out to supplement his menu, come what may. There were three possibilities: a Care package, for which one needed friends or relatives in America. These packages kept a considerable number of people above water during the worst time. We knew no one and did not receive any packages. Then there was the black market for goods stolen from the occupation forces. This was a terribly expensive way of obtaining food. Many Americans and Germans who had their hands on sources of supply grew extremely wealthy in this way. the prices—500 marks for a half pound of butter, five marks for a cigarette—could not be earned in a normal way, with an average income of a hundred marks a week. The ultimate expedient was therefore barter. Go to the farmer, give him what he needs badly and cannot buy, and you'll get something to eat in exchange. Give the Polish black marketeer your old radio; he'll give you two pounds of coffee. Give that coffee to a friend who has ways of obtaining tools; go to the farmer with saws, and he'll give you potatoes and lard. It was also possible to get a job helping farmers at harvest time. Mother did this now and then and brought home a few eggs, fruit or potatoes. Barter was the most successful method, and soon we were all expert at it.

The question of housing was to remain a problem for the next decade. The five of us, for example, were living in three small rooms, but we had the good fortune to have our own kitchen and bath. We fared much better than most people who had been bombed out or had fled from the east. In terms of square meters, we even had more than we were entitled to, and we were often worried that we might be obliged to give up one of our rooms. We lived in the third story of a former villa. Next to us a dentist had set up his practice. Below us, in the best rooms of the house, lived a Communist couple who now felt themslev.es to be on the side of the victors and were given all kinds of support from the Americans. Above us, in the garret, lived the family who owned the house and who had occupied it undisturbed throughout the war. Since it was generally known that they had been privileged, they had become temporarily modest as they waited for their sponsor who was sitting in a special camp for Party people about to be de-Nazified.

As for the problem of work: our family had lost a great deal during the war, but not everything. The state had reimbursed us with money for part of our bomb damage—money that was no longer worth much. The two houses in Cologne, which we leased out and the income from which Mother had been living on, had not been spared. One was in ruins, the other was forty per cent destroyed. We had our indigent grandparents living with us. There was no question of us boys going to the university to study. Hans and I immediately had to earn money, but how, here in Weinheim? For the time being, we were better off in Weinheim than in any large city. Where else should we have lived? Besides, we were happy to be reunited again after all these years. Weinheim was as good a place as any; it was undamaged and an attractive little town. The cities that contained textile industries had all been destroyed, and the industries that were still intact lacked raw materials to make a new beginning.

In order to avoid being sent to one of the nearby large cities to help clean up the rubble, Hans established a firm in which I was his first employee. We called it a firm for the production of craft articles, particularly small paintings. Hans produced them, I framed them, cut glass out of fragments and sold these objects like hot cakes throughout the region, especially in Heidelberg where the Amis were great customers. Shopkeepers practically embraced us for bringing them something to sell. Since there were no nails to be had, I glued the frames with a self-brewed concoction, but, alas, fifteen per cent of the frames fell apart by the time the pictures were delivered. Yet business flourished, and Hans ended up with assembly-line production. He painted on blackout paper which no one needed anymore. We had no idea what all this would lead to, but at least we had made a beginning. With coffee and American cigarettes Mother often traveled to Cologne where she was slowly able to start rebuilding one of her houses by means of barter transactions. We knew it was a time that had to be bridged over. We waited for a change in the currency situation and in the attitude of the victors toward our demolished country. And while we waited, we were determined to enjoy life to the full. We had to make up for the lost war years. We were among the few bachelors of our generation who had survived the war. The girls seemed to know it. We soon had friends of both sexes, many of whom belonged to the local propertied class who had suffered few material losses and whose vineyards were still intact. Thus, we celebrated at the slightest provocation.

With barter goods we dashed all over Germany to obtain food. We came home after countless adventures to sleepy Weinheim where the girls were waiting, where people arranged chamber music concerts, where the Amis slowly became more friendly and gave us coffee for Meissen china, where we took Sunday hikes with Mother into the Odenwald. The period of waiting was a turbulent one, but for us in Weinheim it became a second youth in which we lived from day to day, unconcerned about a nebulous future. On New Year's eve 1945-6 we had champagne. Though the war had been over but a few months, life had us in its grips once again. Since we have only one life to live and these were our best years, they have remained in our memory as such.

However, there was a world outside Weinheim. Even inveterate optimists were unable to come up with any hopeful prospects for Germany. From an internal political point of view, Germany was in a dreadful dilemma. The Allies wanted people in the government—even Communists—who were untainted by Nazism. But who was not tainted? A period of whitewashing, of de-Nazification began. The Nuremberg war-crime tribunal cast the first stone. It was no use pointing out that others were also not without blame. We were all to blame, consciously or unconsciously. Only tremendously strong and uncompromising personalities like Pastor Niemoeller could dare speak of collective guilt.

For us young men it was incredibly depressing. No wonder many entertained the idea of casting off the entire burden by emigrating to a country that was not concerned with all the latter-day threatening world entanglements—perhaps Australia, Argentina or Canada. When we spoke of this, Mother was always in favor of it. She loved travel and had seen a good deal of the world. We were, after all, still young and unmarried. And yet, when we examined these ideas more closely, they turned out to be illusory. No one wanted German refugees. I wrote a personal letter to the Negus of Ethiopia, but received no reply. Moreover, Mother's existence must be assured; her house in Cologne had to be rebuilt. Then our grandparents had to be provided for. The idea of emigration was put aside. It was ten years too soon for that.

EPILOGUE
Cloudburst Over New York

A thunderstorm was hanging over the city. It was five o'clock and offices were closing. People were pouring out of buildings, leaping over puddles, hailing taxis, dashing into subway entrances, jostling their way along dusty office buildings or shiny glass palaces. Some paused a moment in front of window displays; others were accosted by a drunk or a shoe-shine boy, or were saying hello to someone they knew.

"Hi, Jack!"

"Klaus, good to see you. Have time for a drink?"

The driving rain whisked us to a revolving door of the "Sherman," a typical New York bar on Lexington Avenue and 40th Street. It took us a moment to adjust to the semi-darkness inside. There were only a few people on the stools of the long bar. Soon the place would be jammed. The immaculate tables were ready for diners. It was quiet and restful.

"Martini for you?"

"Sure, extra dry—So how've you been lately, Jack? Haven't seen you for a long time."

Jack was always the same; never bothered to answer. In two minutes he would be launching on the subject of his new machine, telling me how good it was and that in four weeks, at the latest, it would be in production. I had been hearing this for the last year and a half.

The man next to me at the bar had an accent one could cut with a knife. He was talking loudly and incessantly, sometimes amusingly. I tried not to listen, but somehow he intrigued me.

"What sort of accent is that?" Jack asked.

"Russian—or rather Ukrainian." It occurred to me that the owner of the bar was Ukrainian and that one had better not mistake him for a Russian.

"What's the difference anyway?" Jack asked.

The loud one overheard it and I could imagine what was going to happen. But the waitress intervened with a plate of hors d'oeuvres. He must be quite drunk; he addressed her in Ukrainian and pinched her. She looked almost frightened, blushed and went back to the kitchen.

"Do you still have relatives in the old country?" asked the man with whom he had been talking.

"No—that is, yes, an old uncle. Sent him a picture post card of New York a few months ago." He gulped the rest of the beer. "Ha, wish I could've seen his face when he looked at that view of Manhattan." He grinned; then his face became suddenly grave. "Poor devil...Well, guess I'd better be going."

The waitress helped him on with his coat. He kissed her matter-of-factly, laughed and departed.

"Crazy guy, that Alex!—Where are you from?" the bartender asked me. "Germany? Oh, Alex talks German too, of course. He's been everywhere. First, German Ukrainian, SS division, then German army, American army Korea, you name it, he's been there.—What is he doing now? Selling office machines; seems to be good at it too." He fumbled in a drawer. "Here's his card, I always have one lying around."

"O.K., Jack. I really must go. You staying on? Well, take it easy. See you."

"Good night, Klaus. Say hello to Barbara and the kids." ,

In the revolving door I realized that I was still holding the business card the bartender had given me. After a brief glimpse, I tossed it into the nearest wastebasket. The name meant nothing to me: Alexander Holuka.

Dear Friend,

Now that you've read my story, I knew you would have many questions to ask. Let me start my answers with the book itself.

I wrote it without using any reference books. I did not have to do any research. I depended on my memory and was supported by all the letters I wrote to Mother during the war. She collected those, and they are now in my possession. So—the story is true with one exception; Alex Holuka is not related to the man in Isbitze and therefore not identified with the boy who lived there.

I wrote this book in chronological order like a diary. I asked Mrs. Schuetze, my translater, to stick to my words as closely as possible. I wanted to avoid misunderstandings. So—here and there it might sound a bit clumsy. Blame it on my instructions to her. Should it ever be published, an editor will have to take care of that. I had no publication in mind, and tried to stick to what happened as I saw it. I also understand your frustrations in not being able to learn more here and there of what happened after the scene changed. But this is life, especially life in the Army. You follow events to a certain point; then you have to leave without being able to look back or to find out. I cannot tell you what ever happened in Isbitze after the train left. My guess is that Dahlig committed suicide after hiding in the railroadman's hut. Frightened and frustrated as he was, he now saw us departing and with us went everything he could himself relate to.

Only a few of those mentioned in the book ever showed up in my life again. General Tolsdorf, my commanding officer in Metz crossed my way after the war in Wuppertal. We became friends. He was one of the highest decorated German war heroes. Ten years after the war he made headlines again in a court action, where he was convicted of having been responsible for a death sentence of a surrendering officer in the last days of the war. From Tolsdorf I learned about American war crimes—tortures—that were later investigated and can be found in F. Utley's book *High Cost of Vengeance*.

Way up in the Bavarian Mountains, near the Austrian border, I ran into Captain Reichenbacher years after the war. I was vacationing there with my brother. We stared at each other in disbelief. We exchanged a few memories—I asked for Ulli my friend—he did not know. Reichenbacher was on the same hospital ship, the "Steuben," wounded in his legs. He therefore was one of the few survivors too. It was hard to comprehend. I was much too close to all this and said goodby forever.

I also met Wallerstein, second man in the assault group. It was after the war in Cologne. We had only our mututal experience, but nothing else in common. We never met again.

Helmut W., my friend back in the days at the textile college lives in

Brussels now and we are in touch. His immediate family survived the war.

Walter Brockhaus, my former student leader, back from the army, switched over to Holland and has lived in Rotterdam since then.

But most of my friends are gone. The school record speaks for itself. We had thirty-two in our class; seven survived the war. One blind, one crippled. One mentally disturbed. Germany's war casualties are not known exactly; they are in the millions - soldiers, that is. Among them, one half million SS troopers, or close to fifty per cent of this organization. But then there were the countless millions of civilians that died in bombing raids and even after the war itself was all over. The Yalta decision to divide Europe forced 14 million Germans to leave their homeland. At least 3 million died as a result of this. Ten thousand, trapped in Czechoslovakia, were brutally killed while human torches illuminated the scene in Prague - something Germans will remember for a long time. We will remember all this because the victims are our people, our brothers or relatives. The survivors are among us to tell the story.

The world will also continue to speak of the six million Jews slaughtered by the Germans. You asked how it was possible that nobody seemed to know about it. By telling my story I tried to explain how much we knew and saw. The average German today even doubts the number; many insist it might be one zero too many. The reason for this is that the percentage of Jews in Germany was so small and that quite a number of those one might have known or heard of showed up again after the war was over. Every German's personal grief and involvement and sacrifice during the war was so major that only a few could get excited—and paid for it in concentration camps - about the disappearance of a Jewish neighbor. The genocide happened way out in Poland, a country as remote to Germans of this time as Saskatchewan or Alberta to the Americans. But this was the place where three million Jews lived among a people as anti-Semitic as they come and only too eager to support the bestial extermination.

Here in the American East the percentage of Jewish people is large, so the involvement, knowledge and personal grief is so evident. The world at large unfortunately shrugs its shoulders about massacres and genocides. Armenians, Kalmucks, Volgagermans, refugee Germans, Vlassowarmists, Indonesian Communists, Biafra Separatists, Sudanese and Vietnamese died by the thousands and millions in this century. If not much is done about it, it is mainly because we have no personal relationship with the victims.

I called my book *Before You Cast the Second Stone* because I wanted the readers to think, learn, know more about and examine themselves before they feel ready to condemn the Germans of this time. The first stone was cast at the Nuremberg war tribunal. I am not equipped to judge this event; but, with most Germans, I am unhappy about the chosen authority, the make-up and the spirit of this court. If it was one of its intentions to plant the feeling of guilt in us, they failed. What we feel is shame and frustration that it happened to us and our nation, of which we have so much reason to be proud. What is left is hope that mankind learns from all this. The best way to better understandings fortunately is followed more and more: to bring people together and learn from each other. This, by the way, is just one reason of many why I am here.

In friendship,

Klaus